# SOLO

*50 classic guitar solos*
*transcribed and explained*
*by Phil Hilborne*

BOOKS

Published by Music Maker Publications (Books Division),
Alexander House, 1 Milton Road, Cambridge, CB4 1UY,
England

This compilation ©Music Maker Publications, 1987

First edition

ISBN 1 870951 00 X

Set 10 on 12 point News Gothic by Camset
Phototypesetting, Cambridge

Layout by Stuart Catterson and Sam Masters

Colour reprographics by CLE, St Ives

Printing by Thomas Reed, Sunderland

Cover illustration by Stuart Catterson

# CONTENTS

# FOREWORD

The solos in this book have been chosen because, when viewed en masse, they represent a good cross-section of both "classic" and contemporary lead guitar styles.

All the solos have been transcribed "literally", which means that in terms of note content, keys, techniques, phrasing and so on, they are as close to the recorded versions as possible. The accompaniments are also the same as their recorded counterparts, except for the solos where no rhythm guitar part appears, (eg. *Edge Of Darkness*); in these, the chord diagrams represent a close approximation of the original keyboard voicings.

The solos have been listed in alphabetical order of artist, not in order of difficulty. If you want to start with the easier solos, I'd suggest that you either listen to the recorded versions, or read the accompanying performance notes. In any case, it is always strongly advisable to work on the solos in conjunction with the records, since there is simply no other way of picking up on the subtle nuances which somehow manage to evade even the most diligently written transcriptions.

In common with any musical transcription, the content of these is inherently subjective and although I personally feel that they are totally correct, you should feel free to make your own amendments and to interpret them as you wish.

I hope you enjoy working through this book, and that you find it a useful tool in the development of your playing style.

Finally, I'd like to take this opportunity to thank the following people: all the staff of GUITARIST, particularly Penny Braybrooke for her excellent editorial work, Lee Hodgson for helping with the music editing, Jon Coombes for his invaluable reassurance, and Sandra and the rest of my family for being so encouraging and supportive.

Have Fun!

**Phil Hilborne**
**Basildon, Essex**
**November 1987**

# INTRODUCTION

The guitar break, or solo, can be an extraordinarily evocative moment in music. But it is also one of the most challenging. It's that point when the guitarist has to come forward, bear his thoughts and emotions to the world and, maybe most worryingly for the player, lay his technique on a platter for the scrutiny of his peers – or those aspiring to that position.

The guitar itself is arguably the most expressive musical instrument we have. Not only does it possess the perfect voice for lyrical accompaniments – Jimi Hendrix's *Little Wing*, for example – but at the flick of a switch, it can utter a spine-tingling ejaculation, like Jimmy Page's solo in *Whole Lotta Love*. Listen to the control of Larry Carlton's *It Was Only Yesterday* or Allan Holdsworth's eloquent *In The Mystery*, the incredible subtlety of *Need Your Love So Bad* by Peter Green, and this seemingly endless variation in players and styles will soon become apparent. In fact, there are probably as many guitar styles as there are guitar players.

Learning to become a proficient soloist represents a mighty struggle. But the tried and trusted formula, attested to by players as diverse as Eddie Van Halen, Eric Clapton and Yngwie Malmsteen, seems to be to listen to those instrumentalists you admire, and learn from their playing. By pulling to pieces solos, fingerings and inversions, analysing finger vibrato – even slowing down the record where necessary – you can gradually develop the feel and technique needed to move on and become a mature and individual player in your own right.

The trap you must be wary of falling into, of course, is the one where you wind up as a watered down, Mickey Mouse version of your idol, building yourself into a little 'clone' box that's harder to escape from than Alcatraz. So it's vitally important to learn from those whose musical ability you'd like to emulate, without becoming their invisible shadow. Better still, take in as wide a range of musical influences as possible (rather than honing in on one specialised area) and your personality will stand a far higher chance of showing through. This, ladies and gentlemen, is where SOLO comes in . . .

Most players will be aware of Phil Hilborne from his columns in GUITARIST magazine. He is a musician of phenomenal facility, technically able to play more or less whatever he wants, and managing it with amazing ease and flair. Phil started playing in bands at about the age of 14, and after about five years of this trained as a classical guitarist and performs the occasional recital even now, but the rock guitar bug had bitten.

Then Phil decided to apply this ability to teaching others. "There was a guitarist in a local band and I thought he was pretty good, so I plucked up the courage to ask if he'd mind showing me a few things. But he dismissed me so callously that I decided, if ever I found myself in the same position, I would never treat anyone else that way. You don't own what you know – it's there to be shared, not locked away like some prized possession. Someone will suss it out before long anyway."

The solos in this book are transcribed with that sentiment in mind, and encompass over 30 years of rock and roll guitar – that great classic, *Rock Around The Clock*, dates back to 1956, while Vinnie Moore's *Lifeforce* is bang up to date. There's a wealth of knowledge to be gained from trying **all** of Phil's analyses, working through the book at whatever pace suits you best – the accompaniments alone should enhance even a good chord vocabulary.

Don't dismiss the 'easy' solos and go straight for the jugular, since as much can be learnt from a single note of Jeff Beck's *People Get Ready* as can be gleaned from many entire pieces.

SOLO is *not* a short cut to becoming a great guitarist. Frankly, I don't believe there is such a thing. But it *is* a wonderful compendium of some of the best guitar breaks ever played, put together by a highly talented player, teacher and craftsman. As Nik Kershaw put it, "I don't know how anybody works that stuff out – that's brilliant. It's extraordinary because they're right. You can tell when you're playing them and you think 'Oh, that's how he does it' . . ."

Nuff said.

**Neville Marten**
**Editor**
**GUITARIST**

# ANALYSING A SOLO

Learning how to play other people's solos can be one of the most enjoyable and rewarding ways of developing your technique and furthering your understanding of not only the styles you work on, but also of music in general. It goes without saying that your objective should never be to 'clone' your favourite players, but merely to use their example as a means of developing your own style.

To obtain the maximum benefit from learning any solo it is most important that, as well as memorising the notes and working on the techniques necessary for their performance, you make an effort to delve deeper and carry out an analysis.

There are two main methods of analysing the note content of a solo. The first is by relating each of the notes in the melody line to the major scale or key of the chord progression. This method usually yields the formula of the scale form(s) used. The second method relates the melody line to the accompanying chords and this shows the vital relationships between the melody and chord progression. If you have any difficulty understanding this, the examples below should make things much clearer. Notice that in each example I have written numbers both above and below the notes to show: 1. the relationship between the melody line and the accompanying chord progression (upper numbers) and, 2. the relationship between the melody line and the major scale (lower numbers).

Before reading my analysis of these examples I would suggest that you spend time looking at these relationships to form your own conclusions as to which scales are being used and how the melodies relate to chords. After you have done this you should then compare your results to mine.

## Fig. 1

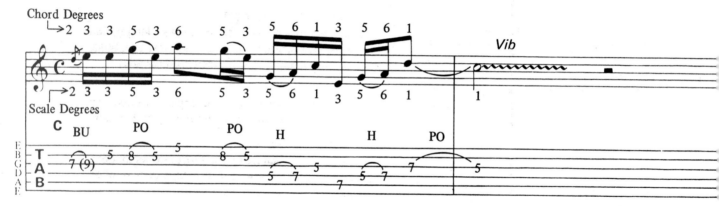

## Fig. 2

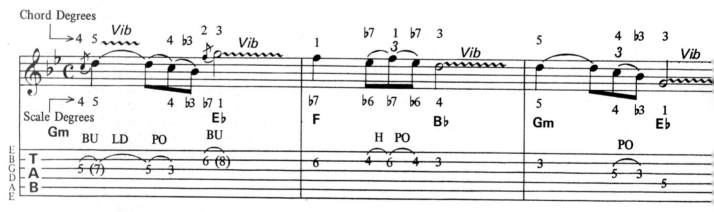

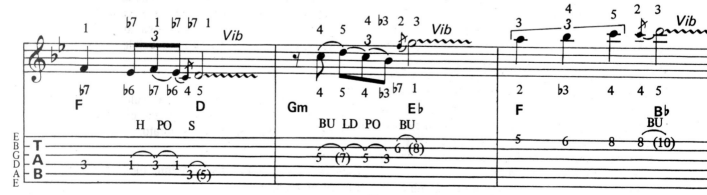

**Fig. 3**

Figure 1 is a two bar phrase in C major, played over a static C major chord. When the notes used are compared to the C major scale (C D E F G A B C) and placed in numerical order, they yield the formula 1 2 3 5 6 which, as you know, is the formula of a major pentatonic scale. In a nutshell, this example is a simple two bar major pentatonic phrase in C, played against the 1, tonic or key chord – C major. As the example is in C and played against a C major chord, the melody/chord relationship is obviously the same as the melody/scale relationship.

Figure 2 features the first six bars of Michael Schenker's solo from the MSG track *Into The Arena*. As you can see, the chords change every two beats which results in a far more complex melody/chord relationship than that of the first example. Be sure to take mental and aural note of this. When the melody line is related to the G major scale (G A B C D E F# G) the resulting formula is that of a natural minor scale – 1 2 b3 4 5 b6 b7 1. Notice from this that although the chord progression is in G minor, you still have to relate the melody notes to the scale of G major to derive the scale form used.

The final example, figure 3, shows bars 2, 3 and 4 of Randy Rhoads' solo from *Flying High Again*. The melody line/major scale relationship (F# major; F# G# A# B C# D# E# F#) yields the formula of 1 b2 2 b3 4 b5 5 b6 b7 1, which isn't a common scale formula. When you meet with this it usually signifies one of three things; either, that the scale is a hybrid or mixture of scales, or that more than one separate scale type is being used, or that there is only one scale type used and any additional notes can be isolated as chromatic 'passing notes'.

In this case the third criterion applies, as the b5 (C) and the b2 (G) both function as passing notes. The deduction of these notes from the original formula leaves 1 2 b3 4 5 b6 b7 1, which is that of a natural minor/aeolian mode as is the case with the formula in example two. In looking at the melody/chord relationship notice that against the D chord the F# natural minor/aeolian mode functions as a D lydian mode. The reason for this is that as the F# natural minor scale is derived from the sixth note of the A major scale, the D lydian mode is similarly derived from the scale, but starting from the fourth note. They are essentially the same, the only difference being the starting point, which obviously causes them to differ in sound.

Another thing I should point out concerning the scale and chord degree numbering on these examples is that the numbers 2 4 and 6 have been used to derive the scale formula, although in most cases, as you have probably realised, they function as 9ths, 11ths and 13ths.

As well as analysing the note content of a solo, there are many other useful observations to be made. To wrap things up I have included the following list of points for you to consider, which I hope will help to further your insight into the solos in this book.

**RHYTHM AND PHRASING**
Look out for things such as phrase length, the space surrounding each phrase, syncopations, polyrhythms and the way notes are accented.

**TONE**
Listen for the subtle tonal changes produced by different picking variations and muting techniques.

**STRING BENDING**
Take note of which notes are most frequently bent, how these bends relate to chords and how often and when the technique is used.

**PICKING AND SLURRING**
Try to evaluate the number of picked notes compared to slurred notes, and the different effects both techniques produce.

**LINE MOVEMENT**
Look for how often scale passages are played in comparison to arpeggios and interval leaps. Also, when playing any solo, make a note as to the number of times you have to jump to a non-adjacent string while playing the same phrase – you may be surprised by how seldom this situation arises.

**GUITAR SOUND**
If you don't already know what kind of guitar, amp or effects are being used you should listen carefully and guess. In fact, it's not a bad idea to try to recreate the sound as closely as possible using your own set up.

**FEEL**
Listen out for the overall 'feel', particularly the amount of emotion portrayed by the phrasing, string bending and above all the vibrato.

**TASTE**
Evaluate how well the solo fits into the overall context of the song.

# A GUIDE TO SYMBOLS AND NOTATION

To ensure that all the transcriptions in this book are as accurate as possible, all the music has been written using both standard notation and tablature. Because of the large number of techniques, fingerings and so on which need to be shown, the information is divided between the two notational forms: standard notation is mainly used to illustrate pitches, left hand fingerings during difficult sections and rhythmic phrasing, and tablature is used to show the exact location of the notes on the neck and the techniques involved in their performance. If you work from only one form of notation and run into problems, I would advise you to consult both the other type of notation and the written performance notes.

## TABLATURE

Tablature is a system which uses a staff of six horizontal lines to visually represent the six strings of the guitar. The bottom line represents the low E string, the line above the A string and so on (the names of the six open strings are shown at the beginning of every line). The numbers placed on each line represent the fret a note should be played at on a particular string. For example:

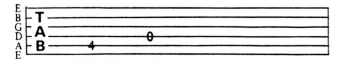

This illustrates that you play the note on the 4th fret of the A string, followed by the open D string.

Diads (two note chords) are shown by numbers stacked on top of each other and unless there is an indication to the contrary, the notes are always played together.

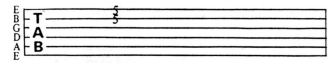

Here the tablature illustrates that you play the notes on the 5th fret of the B and E strings.

Chords containing three or more notes are also illustrated using stacked numbers.

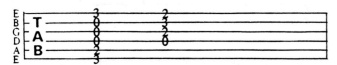

This illustrates the chords of G and D major, respectively.

## TECHNIQUES

The guitar techniques and directions indicated above the tablature and in the music notation are designated as follows:

BU      bend upwards; the string(s) should be pushed upwards, across the fingerboard, causing the note(s) to rise in pitch. The 'target' pitch is shown in parenthesis.

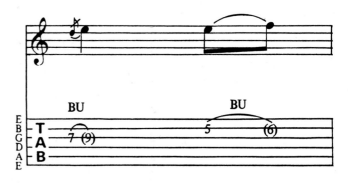

BD      bend downwards; the string(s) should be pushed downwards across the fingerboard, causing the note(s) to rise in pitch. The 'target' pitch is shown in parenthesis.

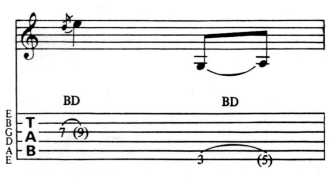

LD      let down; the string is let down after an upward bend. A written explanation is always given if the bend is silent.

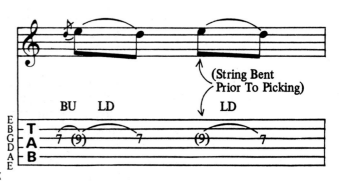

**LB** let back; the string is let back after a downward bend. A written explanation is always given if the bend is silent.

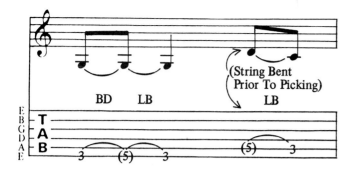

Bend slightly sharp microtonal bend; any bend of less than a semitone.

**S** slide; a left hand slide, either between two specific pitches, or into a pitch from the general area above or below the 'target' note.

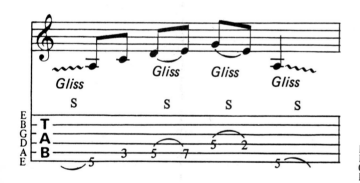

**H** hammer on; the first note is picked and any other (tied) notes produced by bringing the appropriate finger(s) down onto the correct fret with a hammer-like motion.

**PO** pull off; only the first note is picked, all other (tied) notes are produced by pulling your finger(s) off the string in a snapping or plucking motion. The appropriate left hand fingers should always be positioned on the string prior to performing this technique.

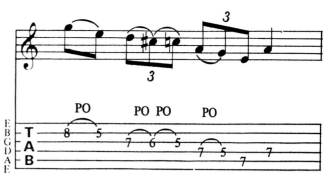

**Tr** trill; a fast hammer on/pull off sequence. The phrasing is always shown in or above the music notation.

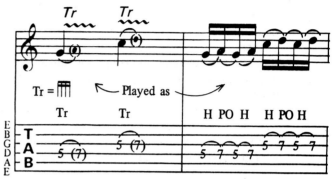

**Vib** vibrato; the string is bent and released slightly a number of times in quick succession, resulting in a 'wavering' or 'singing' effect. The bending motion can either originate from the left hand wrist or fingers.

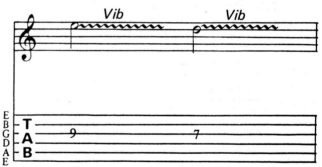

**MU** muted note(s); the notes are usually damped with the right hand palm in order to produce a percussive effect. Severely muted notes are usually bracketed in the music notation.

**(7)** bracketed number; shows a 'target' fret for a bend or a tremolo arm technique. If it's tied to another bracket containing the same number, it indicates either a note of long duration or a note which is sustained across a bar line.

**T** right hand fingerboard tap; notes are produced by hammering the string against the fingerboard with a right hand finger tip. This technique is often followed by a pull off from the tapped note to a note fretted by the left hand.

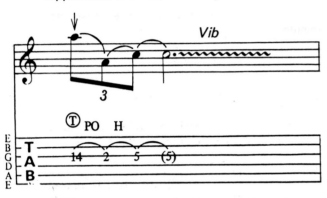

**(L/H)**
**H** left hand only hammer on; notes are sounded by hammering on, without picking, using the left hand only.

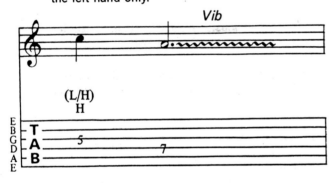

**CO** cut off; a note is stopped prematurely by muting the string with either the left or right hands.

**TA** tremolo arm; this symbol is often combined with others to illustrate the specific tremolo effect required:

**TA LD** – using the tremolo to lower the pitch of a note to another specific pitch

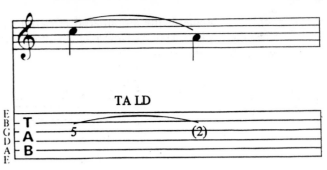

**TA VIB** – vibrato produced via the tremolo

**TA S** – using the tremolo to lower the pitch of a note to an unspecified pitch (dive bomb effect), or playing a note with the bar depressed, and upon picking the note releasing the bar.

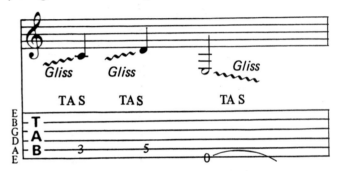

**TA BU** – pulling up on the tremolo to raise the pitch of a note.

**Ph** pinched harmonic; an artificial harmonic produced by striking the string at a node point with the flesh on the outside of the right hand thumb immediately after picking the string.

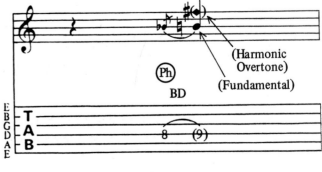

**Th** tapped harmonic; an artificial harmonic produced by touching the string at a node point with a right hand finger.

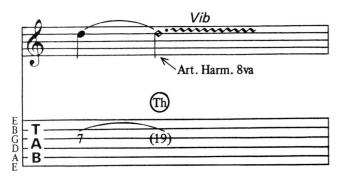

**Nh** natural harmonic; an open string harmonic indicated in the music notation by a diamond shaped note-head (as are all types of harmonic).

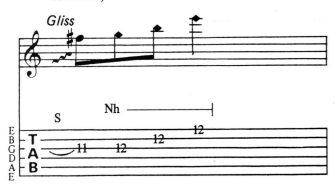

**Rake** glide stroke; the notes are to be played using a single, pick stroke. The arrow indicates direction.

**x** muted string, handling noise pitch or percussive sound.

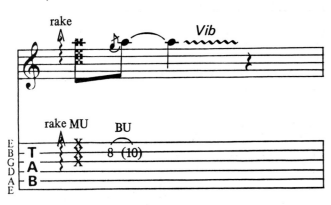

gargle; the effect created by flicking the tremolo arm then allowing it to rock quickly back and forth.

tremolo picking; the notes are picked using alternate picking in the rhythm indicated on the note stem.

**(●)** ghost note; a very quiet or nearly silent note.

**>** accent; this symbol appears above notes which should be accented.

**⊓** downstroke, with pick.

**V** upstroke, with pick.

**Rit** hold back/slow down slightly.

**⌢** fermata; pause.

♩ = 72 tempo of solo in crotchet beats per minute.

**Gliss** ; any slide effect.

grace note/acciaccatura.

**Ad lib** the speed and interpretation is left to the discretion of the performer.

staccato dots; the notes are played in a short/detached manner.

**8va** the music notation is written an octave lower than sounding pitch.

**Loco** the music notation returns to its sounding pitch, after an 8va section.

**16va** the notes are written two octaves lower than sounding pitch. (Please note, you may find this written as 15va in other publications).

Left hand fingering is indicated by:

**T** – thumb

**1** – index finger

**2** – middle finger

**3** – ring finger

**4** – 4th finger (pinky)

**V** Roman numerals above the music notation indicate the position of the left hand index finger.

**CV** full barre; Roman numeral indicates correct fret.

**½ CV** ½ barre; Roman numeral indicates correct fret.

**2 [** partial barre; number indicates required finger.

or strum; arrow shows direction of pick stroke.

Any further signs are explained as they occur, although for standard musical rudiments such as the identification of written pitches, rhythmic notation and so on you should consult any standard theory book. Suggested titles include 'Rudiments And Theory Of Music' (published by the Associated Board of the Royal School of Music), 'A Handbook of Musical Knowledge' by James Murray Brown (published by Trinity College of Music, London) and 'The Guitarist's ABC Of Music' by John W. Duarte (published by Novello).

# CHORDS

All the chord diagrams in this book are illustrated using standard chord 'grids' or 'windows'. The six vertical lines of the grid represent the six strings of the guitar (reading from left to right, E A D G B E). The horizontal lines indicate the frets and the numbers on the left-hand side of each diagram show the fret number each diagram starts from. Open strings are indicated by small circles at the top of the diagrams, and any muted or unrequired strings are designated by an x, also at the top of the diagram.

The circles inside each grid indicate the position of the left hand fingers, and the numbers inside each of these give a suggested left hand fingering. The notes in every chord are shown underneath each diagram and the numbers which accompany these indicate the chord formula; in other words, the notes in each chord in relation to the major scale that corresponds with each chord's root note. A double line at the top of a chord diagram represents the nut of the guitar.

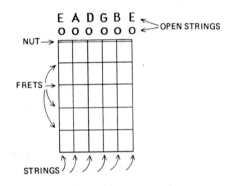

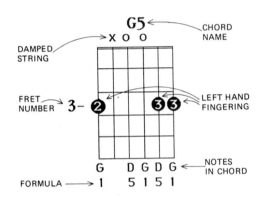

## CHORD SYMBOLS

### MAJOR TYPE CHORDS

| Symbol | Name | Formula | Other Common Symbols |
|---|---|---|---|
| Capital letter | Major | 1 3 5 | Maj |
| 6 | Major 6th | 1 3 5 6 | M6, Maj 6th |
| 7 | Major 7th | 1 3 5 7 | M7, Maj 7, △ |
| 9 | Major 9th | 1 3 5 7 9 | M9, Maj 9, △add9 |
| add 9 | Major added 9th | 1 3 5 9 | M/9 |
| 6/9 | Major 6th added 9th | 1 3 5 6 9 | M6 add 9 |
| 7/6 | Major 7th added 6th | 1 3 5 6 7 | M7 add 6, △add6 |
| 13 | Major 13 | 1 3 5 7 9 11 13 | M13 |

### MINOR TYPE CHORDS

| Symbol | Name | Formula | Other Common Symbols |
|---|---|---|---|
| m | minor | 1 b3 5 | min |
| m6 | minor 6th | 1 b3 5 6 | min 6 |
| m7 | minor 7th | 1 b3 5 b7 | min 7 |
| m9 | minor 9th | 1 b3 5 b7 9 | min 9 |
| m11 | minor 11th | 1 b3 5 b7 9 11 | min 11 |
| m7/11 | minor 7/11th | 1 b3 5 b7 11 | min 7/11 |
| m add 9 | minor added 9th | 1 b3 5 9 | m/9, min add 9 |
| m7 | minor/Major 7th | 1 b3 5 7 | min/M7, m add M7 |
| m7/9 | minor/Major 9th | 1 b3 5 7 9 | min/M7 add 9 |
| m6/9 | minor 6/9th | 1 b3 5 6 9 | min 6 add 9 |
| m13 | minor 13th | 1 b3 5 b7 9 11 13 | min 13 |
| m7b5 | minor 7th flat 5th | 1 b3 b5 b7 | m7-5, m7 dim5 |
| m7#9 | minor 7th sharp 9 | 1 b3 5 b7 #9 | m7 aug 9, m7+9 |
| m#5 | minor sharp 5th | 1 b3 #5 | m aug 5 |

## DOMINANT TYPE CHORDS

| Symbol | Name | Formula | Other Common Symbols |
|---|---|---|---|
| 7 | dominant 7th | 1 3 5 b7 | — |
| 9 | dominant 9th | 1 3 5 b7 9 | 7 add 9th |
| 7/11 | dominant 7/11th | 1 3 5 b7 11 | 7 add 11th |
| 7 b5 | dominant 7th flat 5th | 1 3 b5 b7 | 7-5, 7 dim 5 |
| 7 #9 | dominant 7th sharp 9 | 1 3 5 b7 #9 | 7 aug 9, 7+9 |
| 7/6 | dominant 7/6th | 1 3 5 6 b7 | 7 add 6 |
| 11 | dominant 11th | 1 3 5 b7 9 11 | — |
| 13 | dominant 13th | 1 3 5 b7 9 13 | 9 add 13 |
| 11/13 | dominant 11/13 | 1 3 5 b7 9 11 13 | — |
| 7 b9 | dominant 7th flat 9 | 1 3 5 b7 b9 | 7-9, 7 dim 9 |

## DIMINISHED TYPE CHORDS

| | | | |
|---|---|---|---|
| dim | diminished | 1 b3 b5 | —, °, |
| dim 7 | diminished 7th | 1 b3 b5 bb7 (6) | -7, °7 |

## AUGMENTED TYPE CHORDS

| | | | |
|---|---|---|---|
| aug | augmented | 1 3 #5 | +5, #5 |

## AMBIGUOUS TYPE CHORDS

| | | | |
|---|---|---|---|
| sus 4 | suspended 4th | 1 4 5 | sus |
| sus 2 | suspended 2nd | 1 2 (9) 5 | add 9 no 3 |
| 7 sus 4 | 7th suspended 4th | 1 4 5 b7 | 7 sus |
| 5 | power 5th | 1 5 1 | no 3 |
| sus 4/9 | suspended 4th add 9 | 1 4 5 9 | add 9 no 3 |
| N.C. | no chord is played | | |

# ALTERED CHORDS

There are obviously many more altered chords than those covered by the list of chord formulae shown above. If you encounter any that are not listed, simply follow the directions given in the chord's name, for example, an A7 b5 b9 chord would be an A7 chord (A C# E G) with the 5th flattened and an added flattened 9th. This would yield a formula of 1 3 b5 b7 b9 which, in this case, would have a note content of A C# Eb G and Bb.

# SLASH CHORDS

A slash chord is represented as a triad over a bass note, for example, G/A is a G triad played with an A bass note. The resulting sound in this case is the same as an A11 chord.

Inversions of triads are also represented as slash chords, for example, D/F# is a D major chord with the third (F#) in the bass.

# THE SOLOS

# JEFF BECK
# PEOPLE GET READY

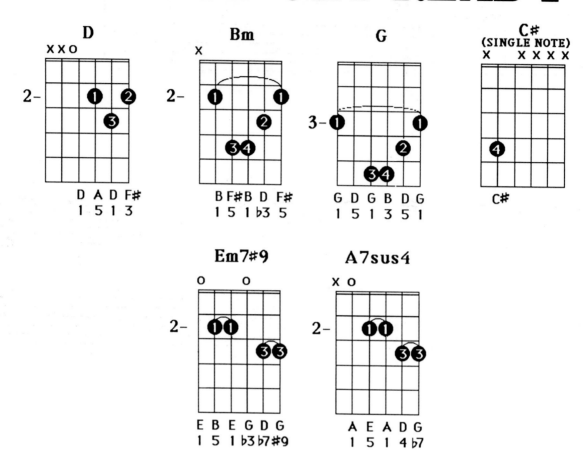

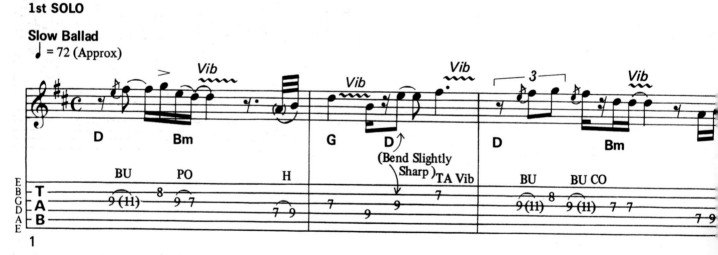

**1st SOLO**

**Slow Ballad**

♩ = 72 (Approx)

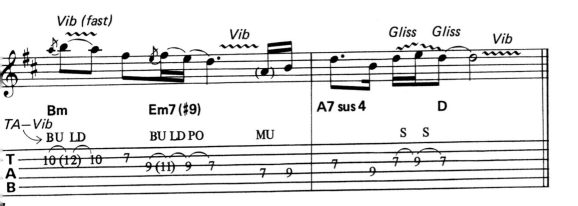

**2nd SOLO**

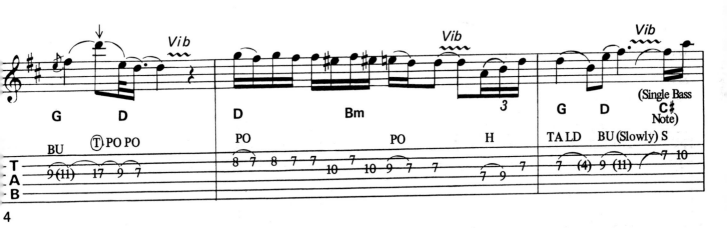

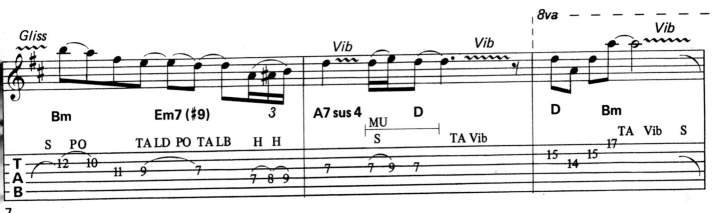

3

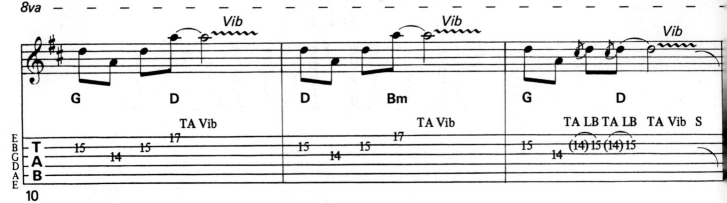

Both solos from *People Get Ready* illustrate one of Jeff Beck's favourite constructional devices – using the solo to embellish and enhance the melody of a song.

The first solo is based on the scales of D major:

| D | E | F# | G | A | B | C# | D |
|---|---|----|---|---|---|----|---|
| 1 | 2 | 3 | 4 | 5 | 6 | 7 | 1 |

and D major pentatonic:

| D | E | F# | A | B | D |
|---|---|----|---|---|---|
| 1 | 2 | 3 | 5 | 6 | 1 |

Jeff actually sets the mood of the song with this first solo which, like the second solo, is very much based around the main vocal melody and many of the phrases are either direct references to it, or slight variations of it. Technically it is very straightforward: the areas which require most care and attention are feel, tone and phrasing.

The second solo also uses the D major pentatonic (shown above) and the only occasions when Jeff departs from this scale form are when he plays the passing note A# in bar 7, the #9s (E#) in bar 5 and the Gs in bars 1 and 5 (G is the sus 4 of the accompanying D major chord).

The phrase in bar 4 may prove rather tricky. I would suggest you bend the E (9th fret, G string) up a tone to F# then, still holding the bend, hammer on (finger tap) the C at the 17th fret with either your second or third right hand fingers. As the string is still bent up a tone the note that sounds will be the D, which is normally found at the 19th fret. You should simultaneously let down the bend and pull off from the tapped note to the E (still held in your left hand) then pull off (left hand) from the E to the D (7th fret, G string). Incidentally, if you don't wish to use the finger tap you could always play the high D on the 10th fret of the top E string.

Bar 7 could also cause some confusion. To play this phrase, pick the E (9th fret, G string) and depress the tremolo arm so the E descends to D. Keeping the bar depressed, pull off from the 9th fret to the 7th – this would normally be E to D, but with the bar held down it is in fact D to C – as the C sounds release the bar so it ascends by a tone to D. Please note, these tremolo arm slurs are not notated, only the melody.

Don't let any of these explanations put you off working on the solo; if you listen to the record you will hear that the phrases in question are nowhere near as complicated as they seem when they are explained on paper.

From the Jeff Beck single *People Get Ready* (CBS A6387). Also on the album 'Flash' (Epic 26112). © 1985 Warner Brothers Music.

4

# JEFF BECK
# TOO MUCH TO LOSE

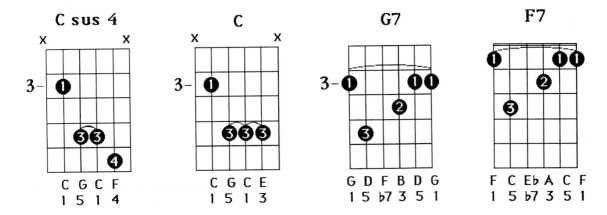

C sus 4 — C G D F B D G — G7 — F7

Moderate ♩ = 104 (Approx)

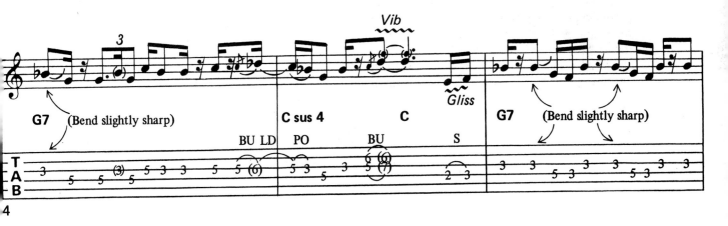

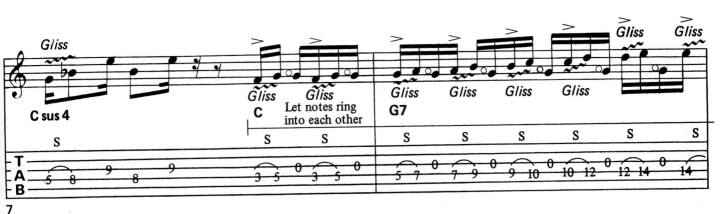

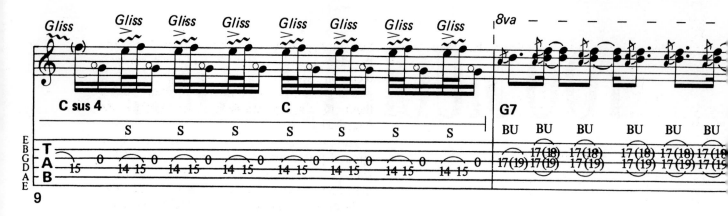

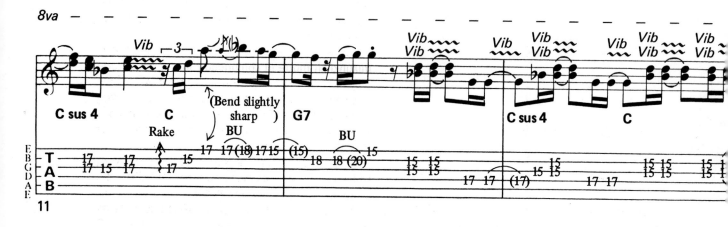

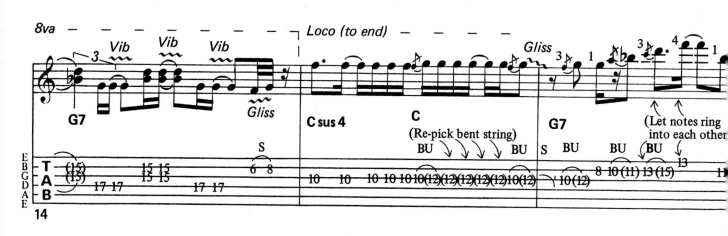

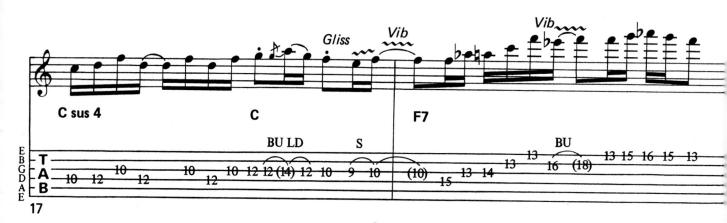

This solo is based around five scales, the G blues scale:

```
G  Bb  C  Db  D  F  G
1  b3  4  b5  5  b7 1
```

the G minor pentatonic:

```
G  Bb  C  D  F  G
1  b3  4  5  b7 1
```

the G mixolydian mode:

```
G  A  B  C  D  E  F  G
1  2  3  4  5  6  b7 1
```

the G dorian mode:

```
G  A  Bb  C  D  E  F  G
1  2  b3  4  5  6  b7 1
```

and the F major/minor pentatonic:

```
F  G  Ab  A  Bb  C  D  Eb  F
1  2  b3  3  4   5  6  b7  1
```

Jeff Beck more often than not shuns a pick in favour of fingerstyle techniques in his right hand approach, using his thumb, index and middle fingers to add a percussive flavour and warmer tone to his solos. You can easily hear the difference such an approach makes in this solo. To achieve the same kind of effect yourself, it is vitally important that you pay close attention to how hard you pick the strings, and the direction in which you pick them; on several occasions the strings should be picked away from the face of the guitar, allowing them to slap percussively back against the fingerboard.

Jeff Beck has always been noted as a great 'groove' player, and the phrasing throughout this solo is a fine example of his natural feel for metrically interesting lines. For example, note how in the blues scale based opening section (bars 1-7) the phrasing is constantly changing and is never duplicated. Notice also how in bars 1-2, even though he repeats the same note, the staggered staccato note phrasing results in an effective musical idea.

The ascending phrase in bars 7-9 uses the G mixolydian mode in conjunction with a pedal tone played on the open G string. As you play through this you should ensure the notes are allowed to ring into each other and that the ascending line, which is played on the D string, is given slight prominence over the pedal tone.

Bars 10-11 feature a series of double stops, which can be seen as being derived from either the G dorian or G mixolydian modes.

With the exception of bar 18, which uses notes from the hybrid major/minor pentatonic scale of F, the remainder of the solo uses notes derived from the G minor pentatonic scale.

From the Jeff Beck album 'There And Back' (EPC 32197). © Epic.

# CHUCK BERRY
# JOHNNY B. GOODE

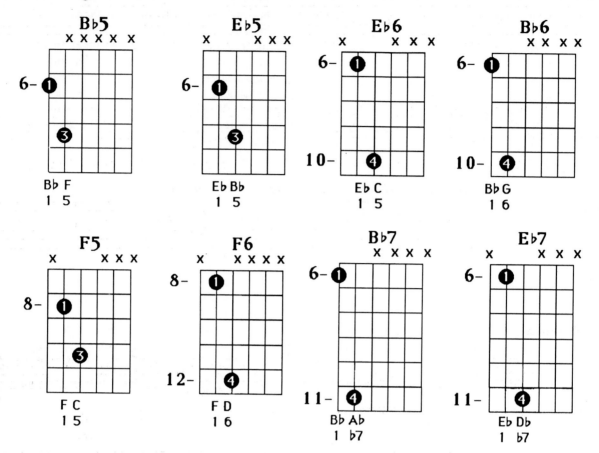

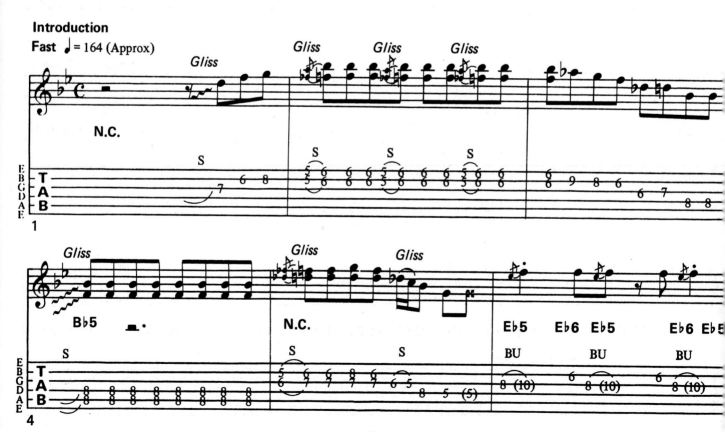

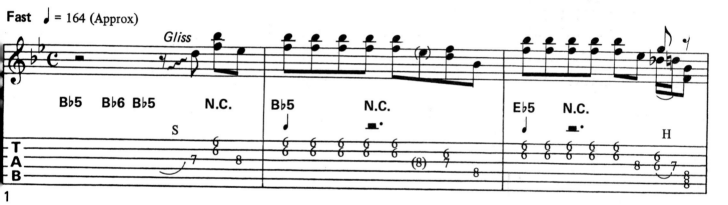

## FIRST SOLO

**Fast** ♩ = 164 (Approx)

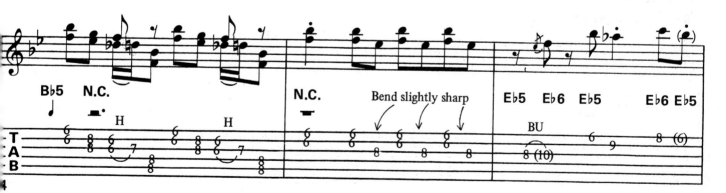

## SECOND SOLO

**Fast** ♩ = 164 (Approx)

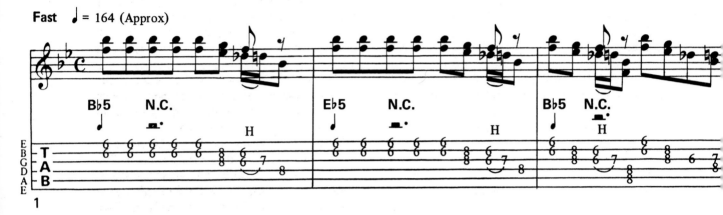

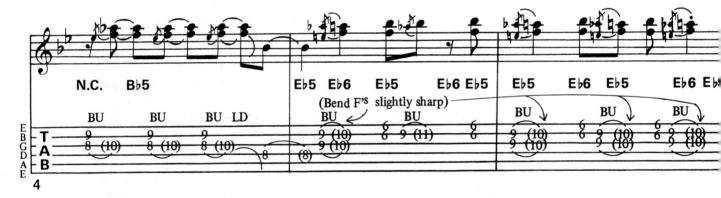

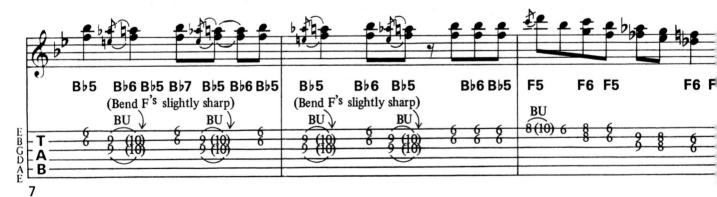

## RHYTHM GUITAR PATTERN

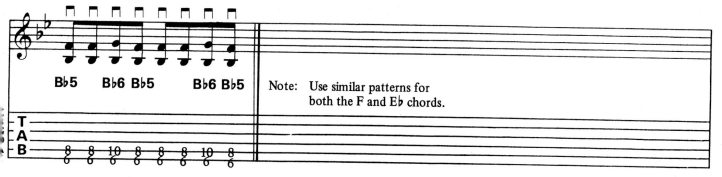

Bb5    Bb6 Bb5    Bb6 Bb5

Note: Use similar patterns for
both the F and Eb chords.

*Johnny B. Goode* is one of the best known of all 50s rock and roll classics. It was released in the UK in June 1958 and only stayed in the charts for one month, although it went on to be perhaps the most covered rock and roll hit of all time. Two of the most outstanding cover versions were those by Jimi Hendrix and Johnny Winter, and the most recent was recorded in 1985 as part of the soundtrack for the film, 'Back To The Future'.

The original track was recorded as transcribed, in Bb – in nearly every other cover version the key is either transposed up a semitone to B, or down a semitone to A – and all three solos are based heavily on this Bb mixolydian mode:

Bb   C   D   Eb   F   G   Ab   Bb
1    2    3    4    5    6    b7    1

As well as this scale form, there are also quite a few passing notes used. The most common of these are the flattened fifths and minor thirds of the accompanying chords.

The introduction opens with a short three note pick up phrase that leads into a series of double stops (two note chords, bars 2, 4 and 5). These are one of Chuck's favourite devices and many different examples can be found in his playing in general. To make them sound effective, you should aim for a clean pick stroke, as this will result in each pair of notes sounding clearly as a single unit.

Bars 6-9 contain a simple repeating riff idea. Notice how the phrasing helps to add propulsion and 'swing' to the idea.

In bar 11 the raked chord (Bb) should be played with a downstroke, making sure that all the notes can be heard clearly and are phrased correctly.

Both the first and second solos begin with similar opening phrases and there are a couple of points of interest here. Firstly, notice the cliche minor/major third hammer ons that occur at the end of nearly every phrase and secondly, notice how the chords that are emphasised by the band are also accented by the solo guitar.

In bar 5 of the first solo all the E flats should be bent slightly sharp until they nearly reach E. The double note bends in bar 11 are similar; in these, the lower note of each pair (Eb) is bent up slightly higher than the notated semitone, nearly reaching F.

Bars 5-8 of the second solo contain yet more double note bends and in common with those just discussed above, the lower note is bent slightly sharp of the notated pitch. Notice also how you are bending b5 and b7 up to 5 and 7 against the Bb chord, and how this second chord produces a tension which is resolved when the following double stop of Bb and F (1 and 5) is played.

As the chordal accompaniment to these solos is comprised entirely of diads, the names given to the chords indicate only the size of each interval used.

Incidentally, the solos were probably played on a Gibson 335.

From the album 'Chuck Berry, 22 Rock and Roll Classics' (CHESS 9286/690BD) © IMP.

# RITCHIE BLACKMORE
# SMOKE ON THE WATER

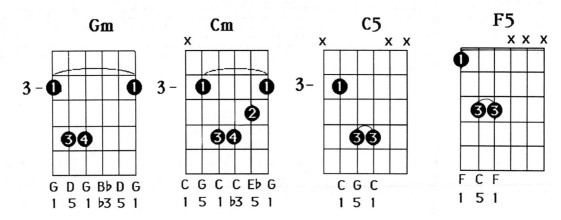

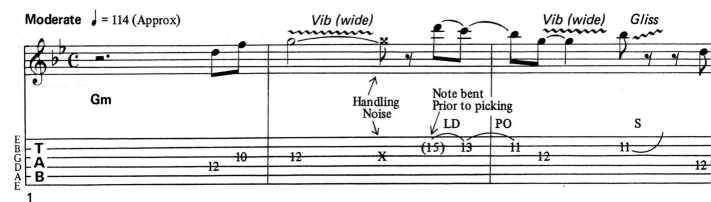

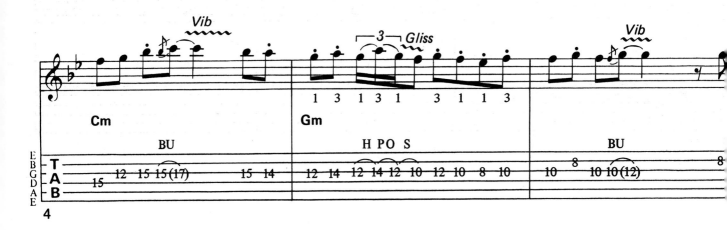

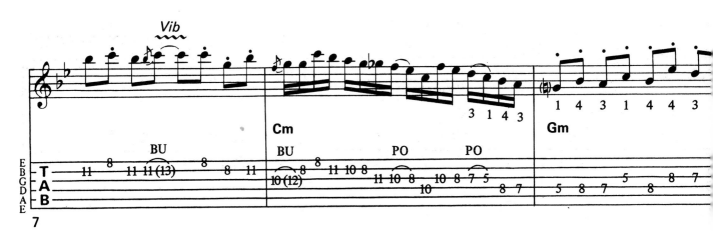

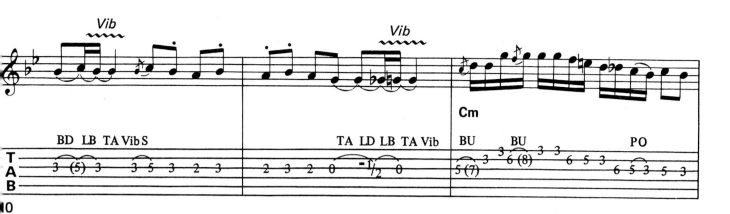

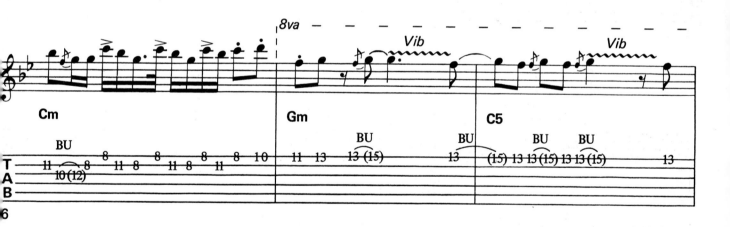

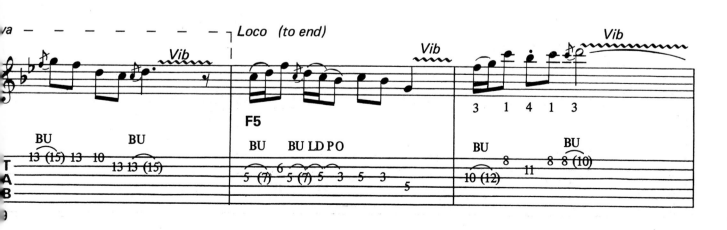

13

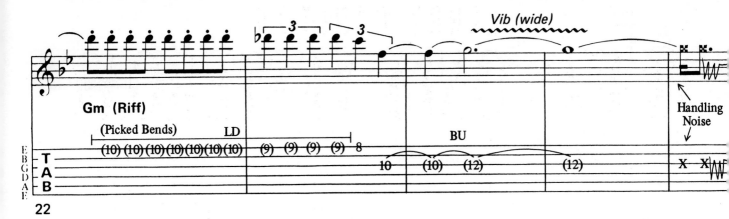

Gm (Riff)

(Picked Bends)    LD

Handling
Noise

**RIFF:**

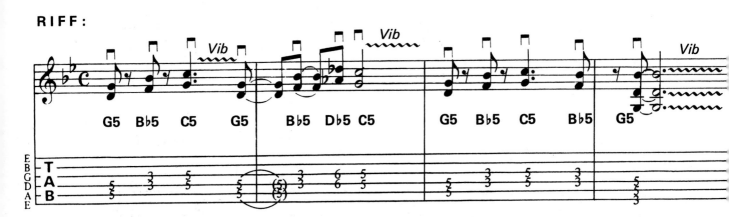

G5  Bb5  C5  G5   Bb5  Db5  C5   G5  Bb5  C5  Bb5 G5

The run down of scales used in this classic solo is as follows. Bars 1-3, 13-15 and 17-26 use the G minor pentatonic scale:

| G | Bb | C | D | F | G |
|---|----|---|---|---|---|
| 1 | b3 | 4 | 5 | b7 | 1 |

Bars 4-7 and 9-11 are in G natural minor/aeolian mode:

| G | A | Bb | C | D | Eb | F | G |
|---|---|----|---|---|----|---|---|
| 1 | 2 | b3 | 4 | 5 | b6 | b7 | 1 |

Bar 8 is in C dorian, with an added b5:

| C | D | Eb | F | Gb | G | A | Bb | C |
|---|---|----|---|----|---|---|----|---|
| 1 | 2 | b3 | 4 | b5 | 5 | 6 | b7 | 1 |

Bar 12 uses G dorian with an added b5:

| G | A | Bb | C | Db | D | E | F | G |
|---|---|----|---|----|---|---|---|---|
| 1 | 2 | b3 | 4 | b5 | 5 | 6 | b7 | 1 |

and bar 16 uses C minor pentatonic:

| C | Eb | F | G | Bb | C |
|---|----|---|---|----|---|
| 1 | b3 | 4 | 5 | b7 | 1 |

Apart from the flattened fifths already mentioned another couple of passing notes are used, namely Gb/F# (major seventh) in bar 11 and the Dbs (b5s) in bar 23.

One of the main features of this solo is Ritchie's use of staccato eighth notes. These are indicated by the dots shown either above or below the music notation and should always be observed very carefully as they are vitally important to the effectiveness of the solo.

In bar 11 the ½ designation in the tab indicates that the tremolo arm should be depressed to lower the open G by a half-step, or semitone, thus producing the notated Gb.

The fast sixteenth note passages in bars 8 and 12 should be picked (alternate picking) very lightly in order to produce the 'smooth' effect that can be heard on the record.

The solo, incidentally, was played on a Fender Strat with a scalloped (hollowed out) fingerboard, through Marshall amps.

# LARRY CARLTON
# IT WAS ONLY YESTERDAY

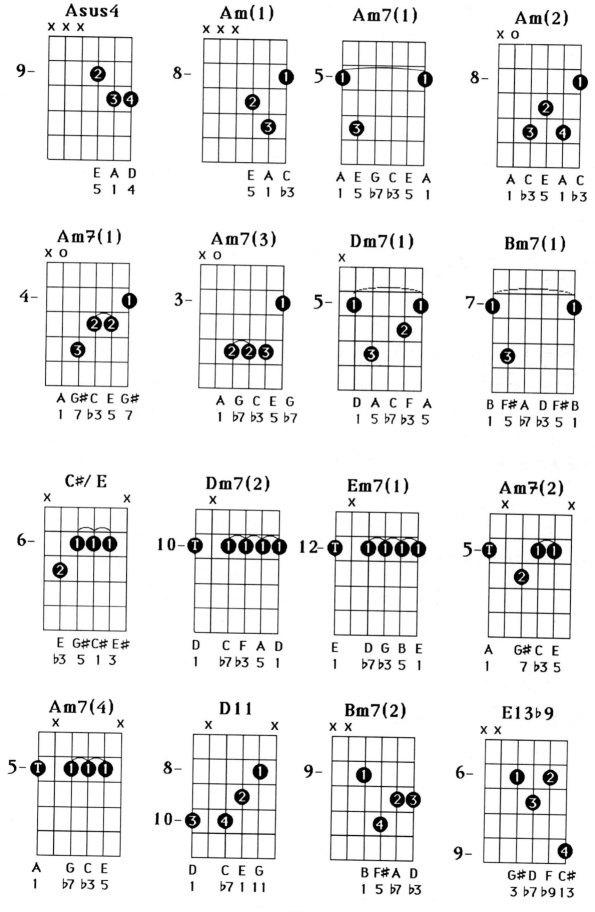

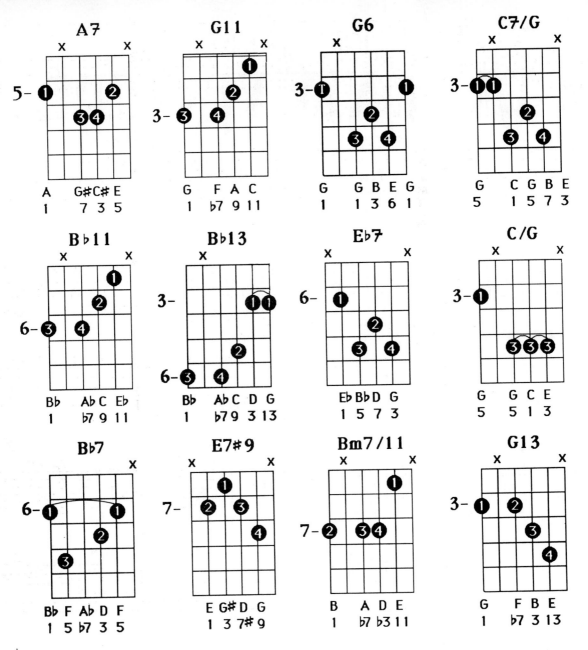

Moderate ♩ = 120 (Approx)

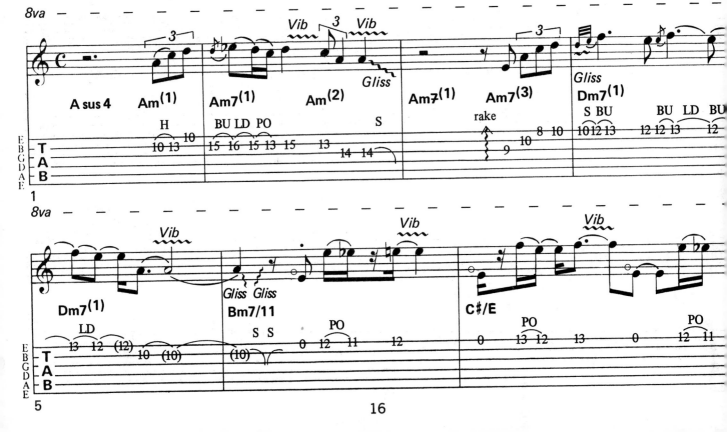

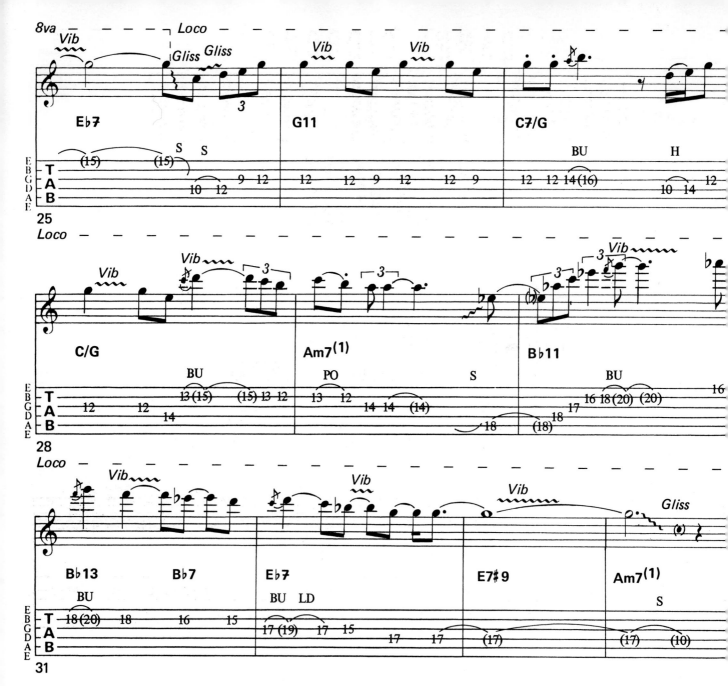

As a player Larry Carlton is renowned for his smooth tone, articulate phrasing and accurately controlled string bending. All three facets are well represented in this solo, which is a reflective piece taken from Larry Carlton's second solo album, 'Larry Carlton'. The solo is not particularly scale orientated, relying more on chord tones than scalular ideas. If analysed in terms of scales, however, bars 1-13 could be seen as using the A aeolian mode/natural minor scale, with added b5:

| A | B | C | D | Eb | E | F | G | A |
|---|---|---|---|----|---|---|---|---|
| 1 | 2 | b3 | 4 | b5 | 5 | b6 | b7 | 1 |

bars 14-17 as using the A melodic/jazz minor scale, with b5/major 3:

| A | B | C | C# | D | Eb | E | F# | G# | A | (ascending) |
|---|---|---|----|---|----|---|----|----|---|-------------|
| 1 | 2 | b3 | 3 | 4 | b5 | 5 | 6 | 7 | 1 | |

| A | G | F | E | Eb | D | C# | C | B | A | (descending) |
|---|---|---|---|----|---|----|---|---|---|--------------|
| 1 | b7 | b6 | 5 | b5 | 4 | 3 | b3 | 2 | 1 | |

and bars 18-21 and 26-28, the G mixolydian mode:

| G | A | B | C | D | E | F | G |
|---|---|---|---|---|---|---|---|
| 1 | 2 | 3 | 4 | 5 | 6 | b7 | 1 |

A common feature of Larry's playing is to superimpose one arpeggio form against another. In bars 22-23, for example, the arpeggio figures are based around an Ab9 chord, while the accompanying chords are Bb11/Bb13 respectively. In this context the Ab9 arpeggio can be seen as a Bb13 arpeggio, starting on the b7 (Ab).

The open string phrases in bars 14, 15 and 16 are rhythmically complex and may prove difficult to perform in time. If so, work on this section in conjunction with the record.

To analyse the solo further I would suggest that you compare the notes in the accompanying chords to the melody line, looking especially at how effortlessly Larry negotiates the chord changes and at the different types of chord/melody relationships involved.

Finally, this solo was played on a Gibson ES335, probably through a MESA/Boogie amp.

Taken from the album 'Larry Carlton' ©WEA. (WEA K56548)

# DANNY CIDRONE
# ROCK AROUND THE CLOCK

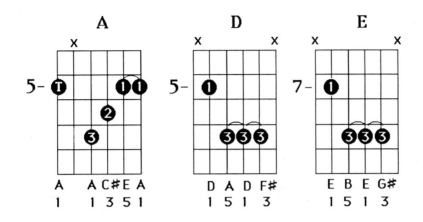

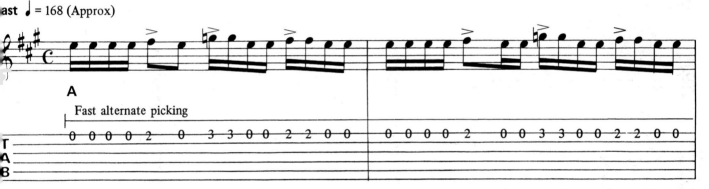

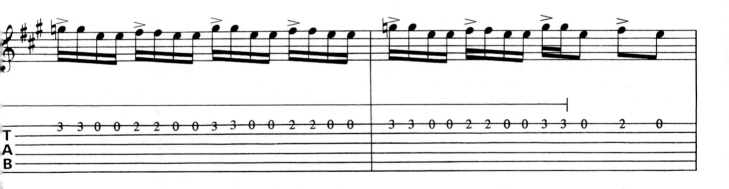

*Rock Around The Clock* is one of the most successful and influential fifties' rock and roll singles. It was recorded by Bill Haley and The Comets on the 12th April 1954, during the same session as their earlier hit *Shake Rattle And Roll* , and was released in the UK in January 1955.

Its initial release didn't make too much of an impression, however, and success only really came at the track's re-release in October of the same year, when it remained in the UK singles chart for four months. This greater interest was probably prompted by the single's huge success in the USA, where it was number one from 29th June to 17th August 1955. One year later, in 1956, it appeared in the soundtrack of 'Blackboard Jungle', and in so doing went down in history as the first rock and roll song ever to be used in a motion picture soundtrack. The track was later re-released and had more UK chart success, in 1968 and 1974.

The guitar solo was played by Danny Cidrone – later replaced in the Comets by Fran Beecher – and by today's standards it's fairly straightforward. Provided you have a reasonably solid picking technique it shouldn't present any problems.

The scale used is the A minor/major pentatonic with an added b5:

| A | B | C | C# | D | Eb | E | F# | G | A |
|---|---|---|----|---|----|---|----|---|---|
| 1 | 2 | b3 | 3 | 4 | b5 | 5 | 6 | b7 | 1 |

The solo begins with a fairly typical tremolo picked open string pedal idea (bars 1-4). During this, the sixth and flattened seventh (F# and G) are alternated with the pedal note of E (fifth of the A chord).

The second section – bars 5-6 – is a simple repeating one bar phrase, during which the sixth of the D chord (B) is notated as being bent up a semitone to the flattened seventh (C), although the actual bend is only of about a quartertone and thus defies conventional notation. To achieve the correct effect, make sure you only push the string up very slightly.

Bar 7 begins with the root and fifth of the A chord (A and E) played as an ending to the preceding two bar phrase. The last quaver of bar 7 and the first two beats of bar 8 feature the textbook rock and roll cliche of a minor to major third hammer-on (C-C#), followed by a fifth to sixth hammer-on (E-F#) ending up with the root (A). A more or less identical example of this can be found on the introduction to Eric Clapton's version of *Further On Up The Road*.

Bars 9 and 10 consist of a sixteenth note figure which descends across the E, B, G and D strings using the same pattern across all four strings. If you analyse the notes in relation to the E chord you will see that some of them are 'outside', or dissonant, to the accompanying harmony (D# and C, for example). However, as the passage is played quickly these notes only add chromatic 'colour' and their true dissonance is not particularly audible.

The closing phrase in bars 11-12 leads nicely back to the song by using a root, third, fourth and fifth bass line idea, which is phrased using the standard 'jazzy' dotted eighth/sixteenth 'swing' rhythm.

From the Bill Haley & The Comets compilation album 'Rock Around The Clock' (Hallmark SHM 68). ©1954 Ed Kassner Music Company Ltd.

# ERIC CLAPTON
# DOUBLE CROSSIN' TIME

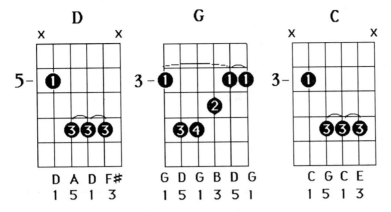

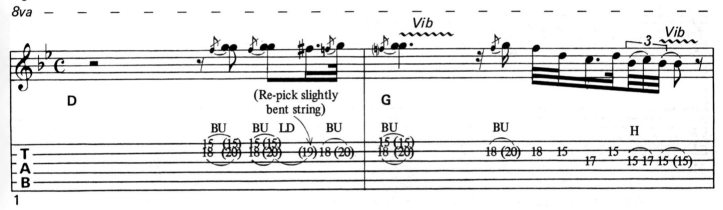

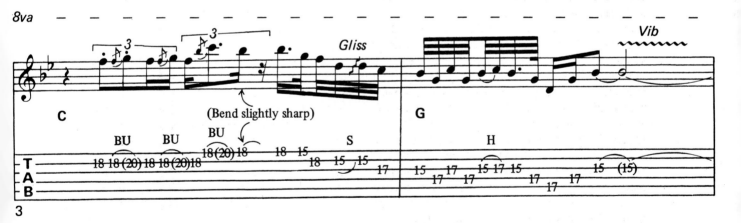

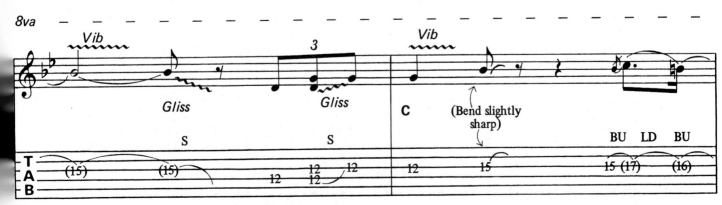

DOUBLE CROSSIN' TIME — Accompanying Guitar Part

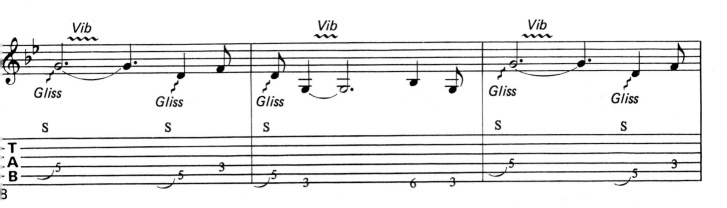

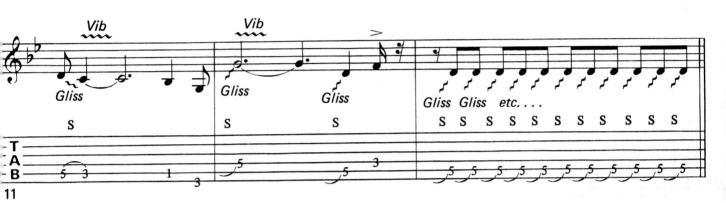

The solo on *Double Crossin' Time* is played over a straightforward twelve bar blues progression in G, using the G minor pentatonic:

G  Bb  C  D  F  G
1  b3  4  5  b7  1

the G blues scale:

G  Bb  C  Db  D  F  G
1  b3  4  b5  5  b7  1

and the C mixolydian mode:

C  D  E  F  G  A  Bb  C
1  2  3  4  5  6  b7  1

It basically consists of a number of short phrases which are either isolated individual riff ideas, or based on a question/answer format. As the solo was most likely improvised, 'feel' rather than metrical accuracy is undoubtedly the main consideration, thus although the underlying pulse is in 12/8 many of the phrases go across this and even when notated in the slightly more accommodating time signature of 4/4, remain rhythmically complex and result in some pretty difficult figures. If you encounter problems reading the notational phrasing – which incidentally should only be treated as a guide – I would suggest that you work closely with the record and instead of learning the solo by rote that you digest the ideas as accurately as possible then manipulate them to suit your own taste and style. After all, what's really important about the blues, as with nearly all music, is the spirit, feeling and ideas behind it and not necessarily just the ability to reproduce perfect versions of other people's improvisations.

The first phrase (bars 1-2) comprises some fairly typical double note bends. These are broken up in bar 1 by a double note bend (F-G) which upon reaching the G is let down by a semi-tone to produce the notated F# (major 7th). If you find this difficult, check you are reaching the correct pitch by playing the F# (19th fret, B string), then comparing this to the let-down bend in the phrase.

Bars 2-5 contain a pair of minor pentatonic phrases. Notice how in the second phrase (bar 3) Eric bends the b3 slightly sharp (see also bars 6, 7 and 12). This b3 nearly reaches the major third but stops just short, resulting in a rather interesting bluesy, quarter tone effect.

Following the short triplet idea in bar 5 is an idea using notes from the C mixolydian mode (bars 6-7). In this, notice how the first bend is let down to the major seventh of the accompanying C chord (B) and how in the following bar (bar 7) all the Bs are flattened to produce a more characteristic b7 effect.

Apart from the blues scale phrases in bars 10-11, the remainder of the solo uses similar ideas and devices to those already discussed. One further point of interest, however, is that instead of ending the solo high up the neck as is common practice in many solos, Eric chose to drop down to the third position for his closing phrase.

The solo was played on a Gibson Les Paul, possibly through a Marshall amp. To hear it clearly, listen to the right hand stereo channel, as the solo was mixed totally to that side.

From the album 'John Mayall's Bluesbreakers', with Eric Clapton/Decca SKL/ 4804.

# ERIC CLAPTON
# EDGE OF DARKNESS

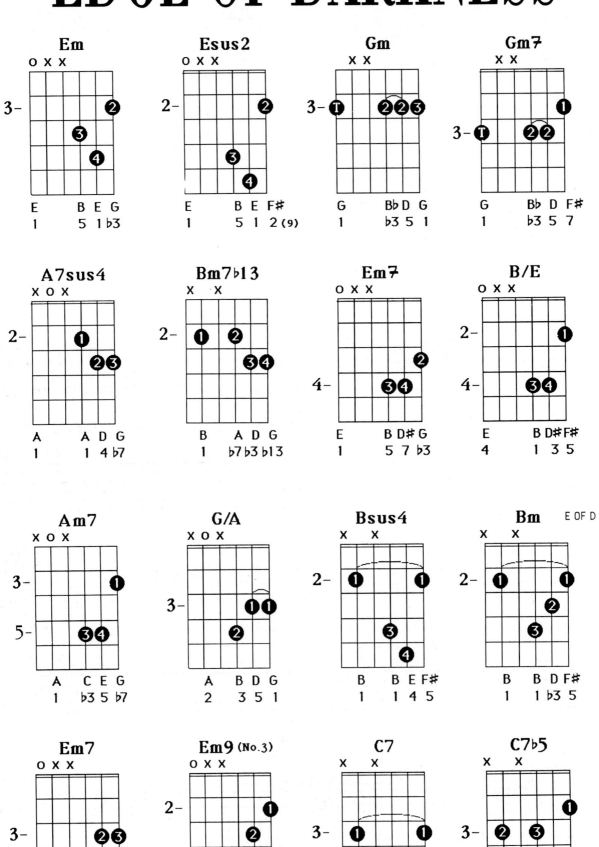

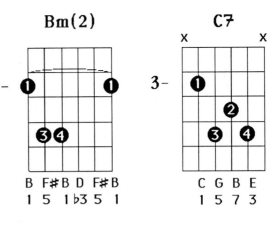

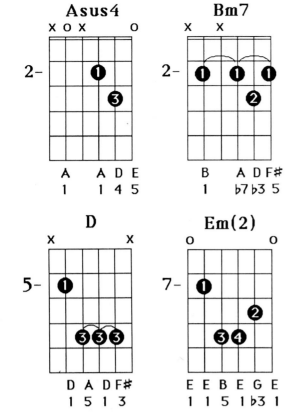

NOTE;- Play all chords using either finger style, or a pick/finger style combination.

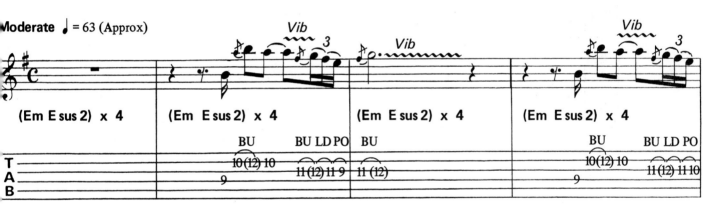

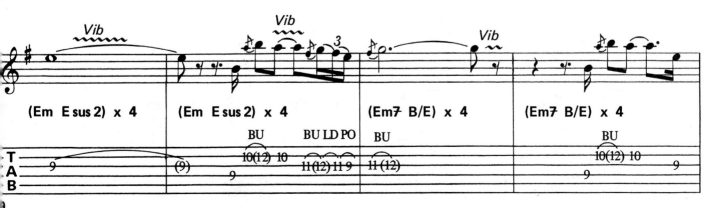

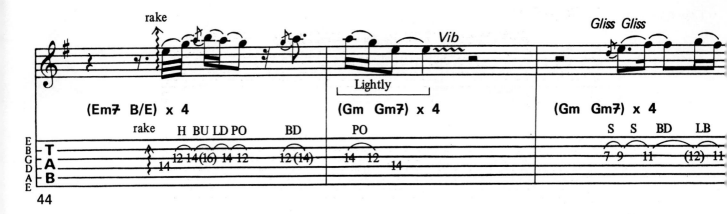

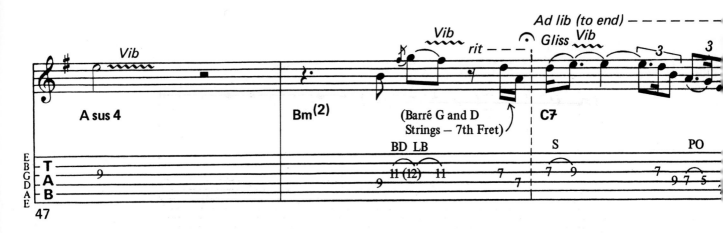

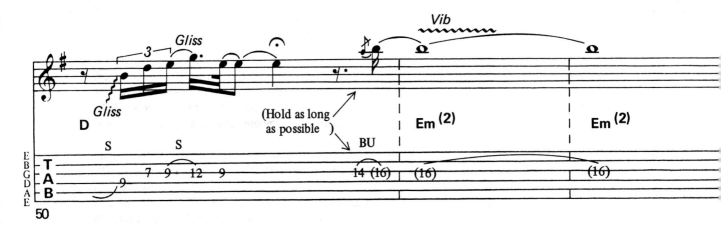

EDGE OF DARKNESS — ACCOMPANIMENT SUGGESTIONS

**1. Em — E sus 2**

### 2. Gm – Gm7

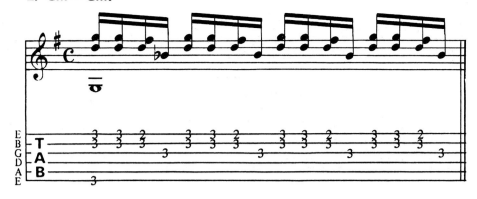

### 3. A7 sus 4

Note :– Use patterns similar to these,
for all remaining chord voicings.

For this solo Eric uses the E minor pentatonic scale:

| E | G | A | B | D | E |
|---|---|---|---|---|---|
| 1 | b3 | 4 | 5 | b7 | 1 |

and the E aeolian mode/natural minor scale;

| E | F# | G | A | B | C | D | E |
|---|----|---|---|---|---|---|---|
| 1 | 2 | b3 | 4 | 5 | b6 | b7 | 1 |

As this is a sensitive and atmospheric piece great care should be taken over dynamics, phrasing and vibrato. From bars 37-52 I have indicated the dynamics beneath the music notation; try to follow these as closely as possible. Also, to duplicate the vibrato correctly, especially on the bends, listen closely to the record and try to capture the subtle nuances.

In bars 3, 5, 6, 8 and 11 the semitone bends can also be played by bending downwards instead of upwards as indicated. Experiment with both methods and employ the one you find most comfortable.

You may find some of the rhythms on the music notation difficult to read. If so it may help you to work them out aurally from the record. This is particularly applicable to bars 31-32 and 34-35, which are both heavily ornamented and which, if performed, would not necessarily be played as notated.

The closing segment in bars 48-52 is unbarred. The phrasing here should be treated as a guide rather than taken literally.

From the BBC TV Series 'Edge Of Darkness' (BBC 12RSL 178/12″ single). EC Music Ltd. Chappell Music Ltd/Mother Fortune Inc. Intersong Music Ltd.

# ERIC CLAPTON
# FOREVER MAN

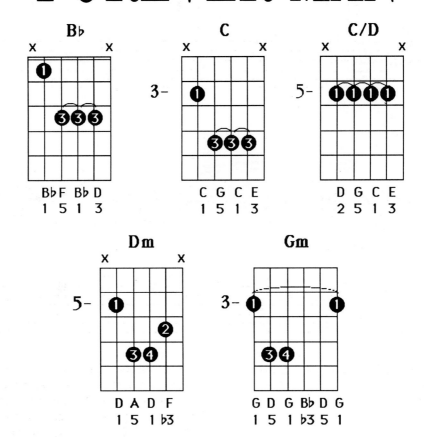

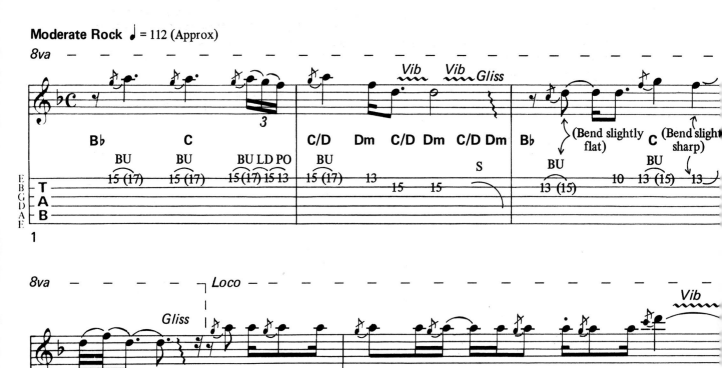

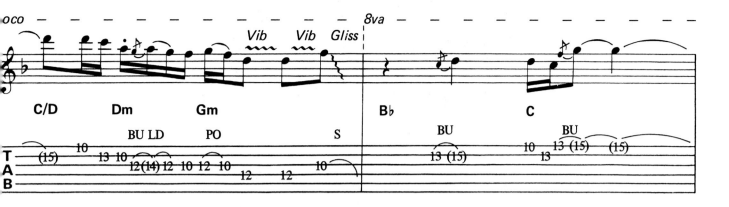

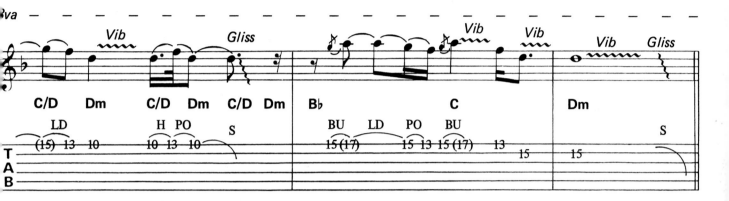

This solo is a good example of Eric Clapton's later and more commercial work. Melodically it is based around the D minor pentatonic scale:

| D | F | G | A | C | D |
|---|---|---|---|---|---|
| 1 | b3 | 4 | 5 | b7 | 1 |

Although in terms of technique the solo is fairly basic, it does incorporate tasteful phrasing and a strong sense of dynamics, which give the piece an exciting quality characteristic of much of today's up-tempo commercial music.

One point worth mentioning is that the D minor chords in the accompaniment for bars 2, 4, 6 and 8 should be hammered on from the C/D chords in a 'funky' style vaguely reminiscent of the rhythm part to the Doobie Brothers' *Long Train Runnin'*.

Incidentally, Eric Clapton probably played this solo on 'Blackie', his famous black Fender Stratocaster through Marshall amps.

Taken from the Eric Clapton album 'Behind The Sun' (DUCK 9251 661), also on 'The Cream Of Eric Clapton' (WEA ECTV 1833519-4). ©SBK Songs.

# ROBERT CRAY
# PORCH LIGHT

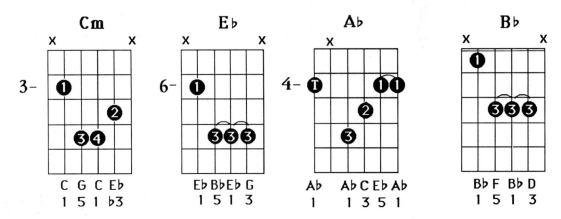

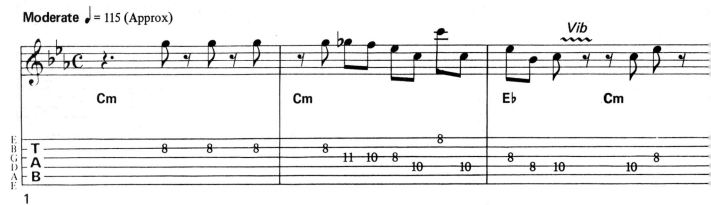

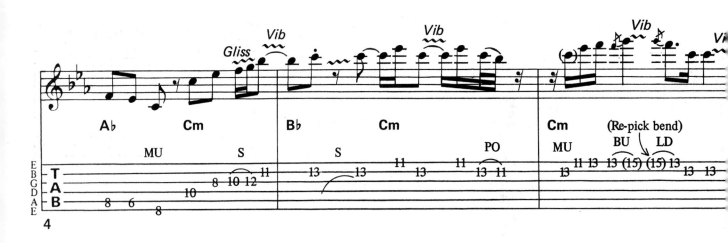

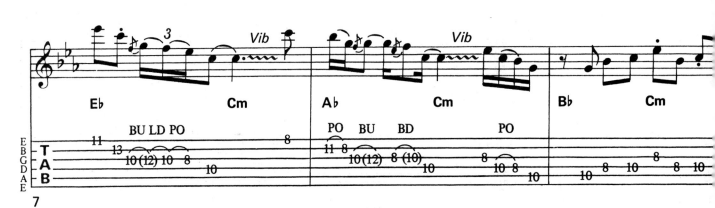

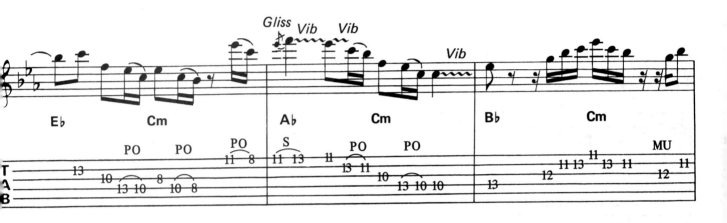

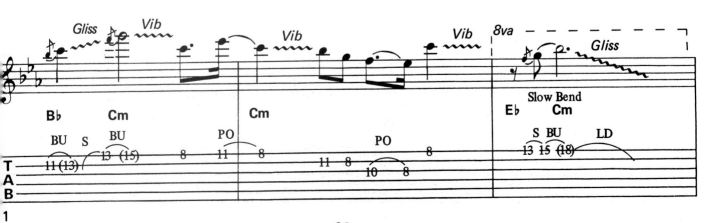

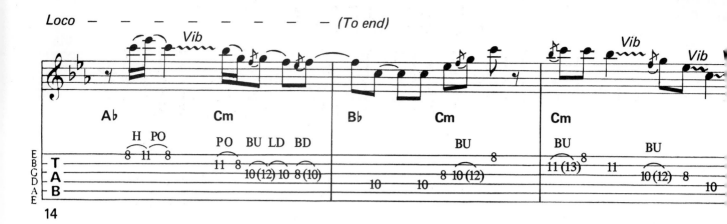

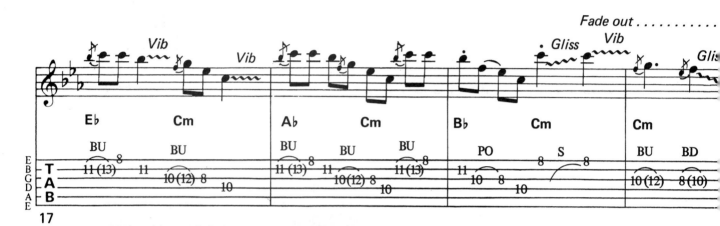

The two solos here centre around the C blues scale:

| C | Eb | F | Gb | G | Bb | C |
|---|----|---|----|---|----|---|
| 1 | b3 | 4 | b5 | 5 | b7 | 1 | (first solo, bars 1/3)

and the C minor pentatonic scale;

| C | Eb | F | G | Bb | C |
|---|----|---|---|----|---|
| 1 | b3 | 4 | 5 | b7 | 1 |

The first solo begins with very sparse phrases through bars 1-3, which gradually become more complex in bars 4-8 before returning to the simple closing phrase of bar 9. Notice how the rhythm of this phrase is identical to the opening phrase in bar 2, and how these phrases give both the start and finish a feeling of uniformity.

The second solo is played using the C minor pentatonic scale (see above), and uses similar phrasing to that in the first solo, in that the phrases are mostly short and 'staggered'. As such they epitomize an important aspect of a typical blues solo.

When I first heard the record I thought the bend in bar 13 went up in pitch from F to Bb! Listening more closely, however, I realised that prior to the bend there was a slide from F-G, and that after this the string was bent up a minor third to Bb. If you play this slide/bend combination smoothly enough it should sound like a bend that ascends by a fourth.

Both solos were probably played on a Fender Stratocaster, through a Fender Super Reverb amp, with the pickup selector in an out of phase position.

From the Robert Cray Band album 'False Accusations' (Demon Records/Fiend 43). © WEA.

34

# AL DI MEOLA
# RITMO DE LA NOCHE

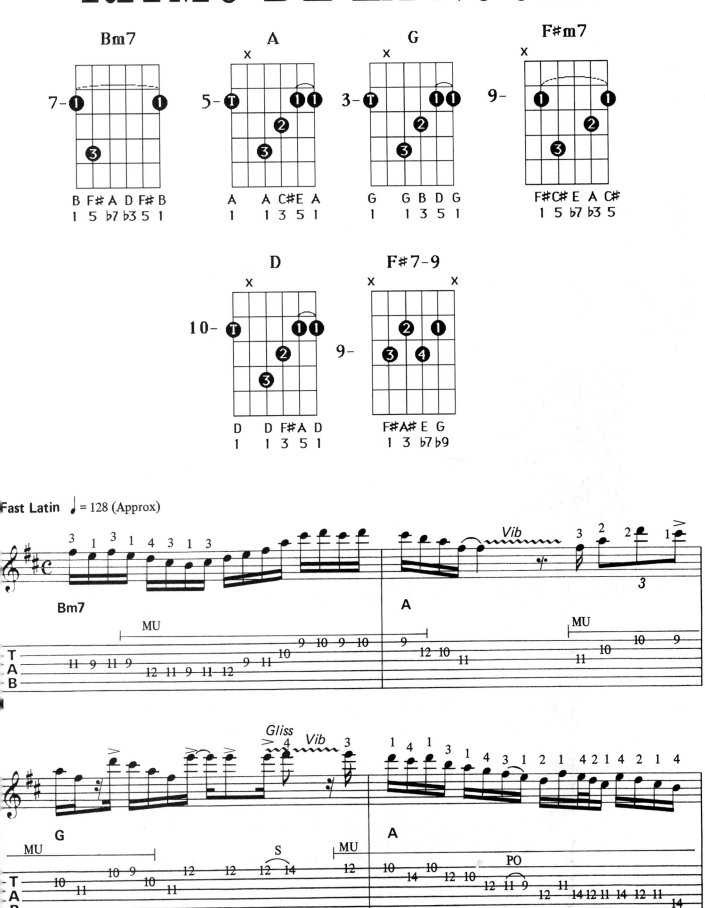

Bm7      F♯7-9      Bm7    N.C.

25

The two scale forms used here are the B aeolian mode/natural minor scale:

B  C♯  D  E  F♯  G  A  B
1  2  b3  4  5  b6  b7  1

and the B harmonic minor scale:

B  C♯  D  E  F♯  G  A♯  B
1  2  b3  4  5  b6  7  1

Al also employs a fair number of chromatic passing note and arpeggio ideas.

One of the most striking aspects of this solo and indeed of Al's playing style in general, is his masterful command of fast alternate picking and percussive muting techniques. In fact, to be able to play through this solo at anything approaching the correct speed I would thoroughly recommend that you memorise the fingerings first, then work with either a metronome or a drum machine, gradually building up the tempo over a period of time.

The solo begins (bars 1-4) with a combination of both scalic and triadic arpeggio ideas (D major and D major 7), which incorporate notes from the B aeolian mode. As is the case with the majority of the first half of the solo (bars 1-13) these are all played with heavy muting applied via the right hand palm. Technically you should ensure that the thirty-second notes (third beat of bar 4) are picked cleanly and without undue hesitation. Failure to do this will impede the flow of the passage and the effect of the rhythmic change will be lost.

In bars 5-9 Al uses the B harmonic minor scale coupled with chromaticism (third beat, bar 5 and fourth beat, bar 7) and more arpeggio ideas (B minor, bars 5, 6 and 7). Be careful to observe all staccato markings and rhythmic figures in this section, as the phrasing is absolutely vital to the overall 'feel' produced.

From the last beat of bar 9 through to the end of bar 12 there is an ascending scale based run, comprised of a series of repetitive three-note figures which are phrased in 'sixes'. On record this sounds far more difficult than it actually is, and the secret to performing it cleanly is to 'look ahead' and mentally imagine the finger placement for each successive figure. Notice also that I have fingered it to be played entirely on the top E string, although obviously it is possible to play it across the strings. If you find my fingering awkward or impractical I

would suggest you work at developing an alternative of your own.

Bars 13-18 feature some fairly straightforward ideas, which should present little difficulty. The only thing to watch out for is the phrasing in bars 17-18, which is quite complex and may be easier to work through in conjunction with the record rather than solely from the notation.

The phrase which runs from bar 19 through to bar 22 employs many of the ideas already mentioned, such as chromatic and harmonic minor ideas. There is, however, an interesting passing note used in bar 22 (F, first beat). This is extremely tense in relation to the accompanying F♯m7 chord, but as it is quickly resolved to the E (b7 of the chord) the dissonant effect is only briefly heard.

Bar 23 is undoubtedly the most demanding alternate picking phrase of the entire solo. To practise this you may find it helpful to isolate each beat and treat them as though they were four separate individual repeated figures, combining them only as and when you feel comfortable.

The final three bars are also extremely difficult to perform at the correct speed, as the notes fall in a pattern which is not only difficult to memorise, but also seems to encourage the left hand fingers to tie themselves in knots! The only suggestion I can make is that you practise it very carefully, always using the same fingering, until you reach a point where you can play it automatically.

# THE EDGE
# SUNDAY BLOODY SUNDAY

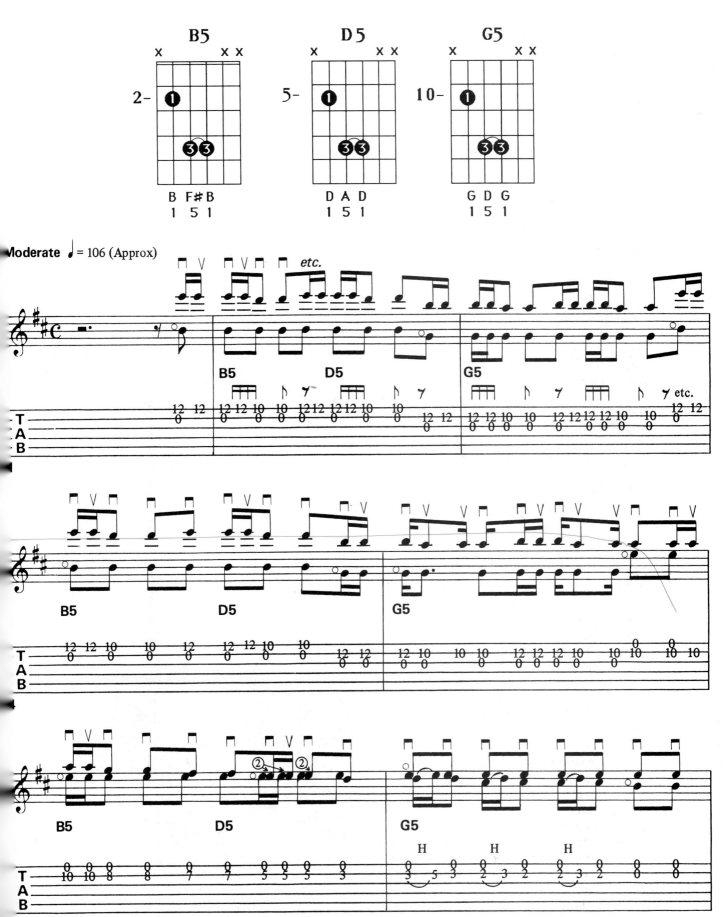

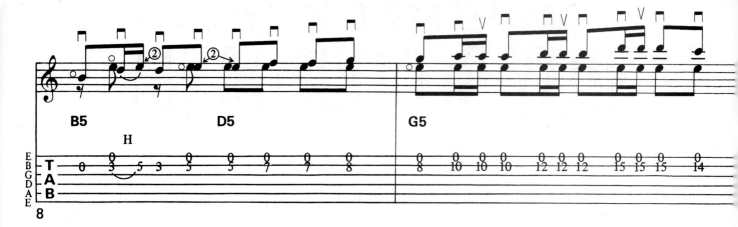

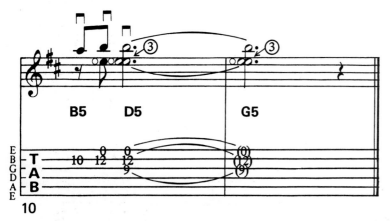

This example of the Edge's playing illustrates his interesting approach to soloing, whereby he plays open string pedal tones both above and below melodic lines. It is a very effective device within the context of a three piece band such as U2, helping to fill out the sound. In this case, it also lends an ethnic Irish flavour to the music.

The scale used here is the B aeolian/natural minor scale:

| B | C# | D | E | F# | G | A | B |
|---|----|---|---|----|---|---|---|
| 1 | 2 | b3 | 4 | 5 | b6 | b7 | 1 |

The entire solo is notated in two parts. The main melodic line remains in the upper part for most of the solo, although the parts cross and the melody line becomes the lower part for the last eighth note of bar 6 (D), all of bar 7, and the first two and a half beats of bar 8. Throughout the solo the melody line should be given slight prominence over the pedal tone accompaniment. The pick-stroke indications are given only as a guide; if you find them awkward feel free to substitute your own patterns.

Finally, the E5 chord is sustained for the last two bars of the solo (bars 10-11) against the accompanying D bass note in bar 10, sounding as a D6/9 and against the G bass note in bar 11 as a G6 sound.

Taken from the U2 album 'War' (ALPS 9733) ©

40

# DON FELDER & JOE WALSH
# HOTEL CALIFORNIA

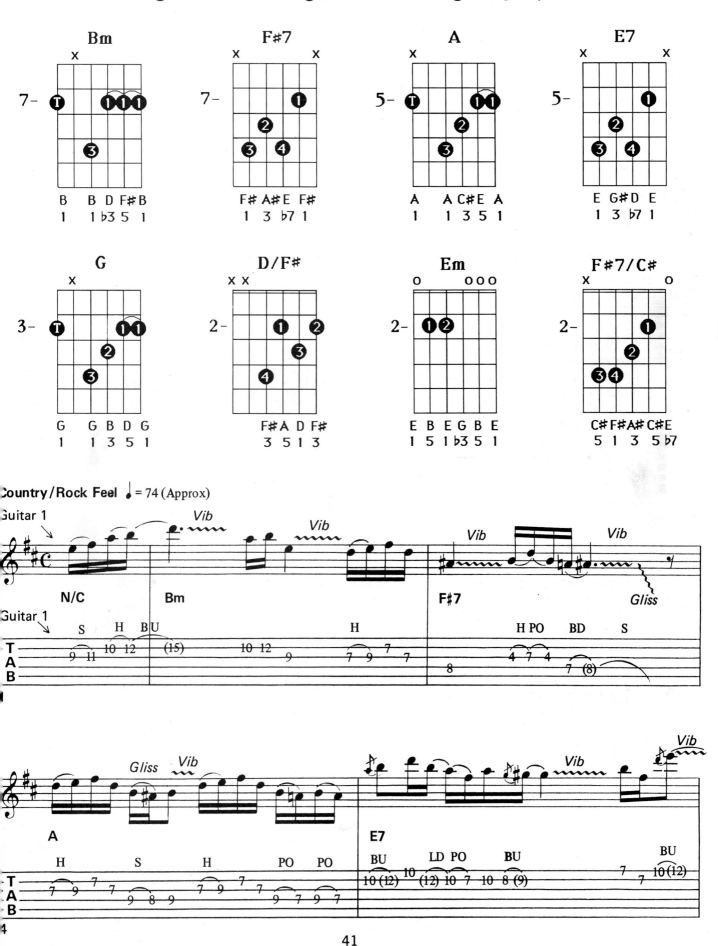

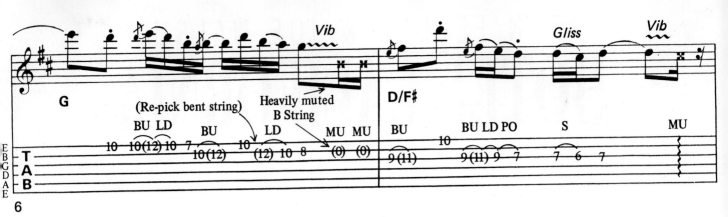

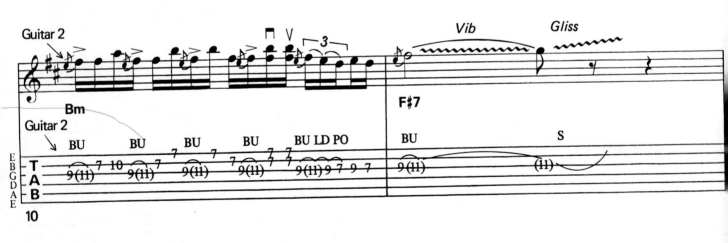

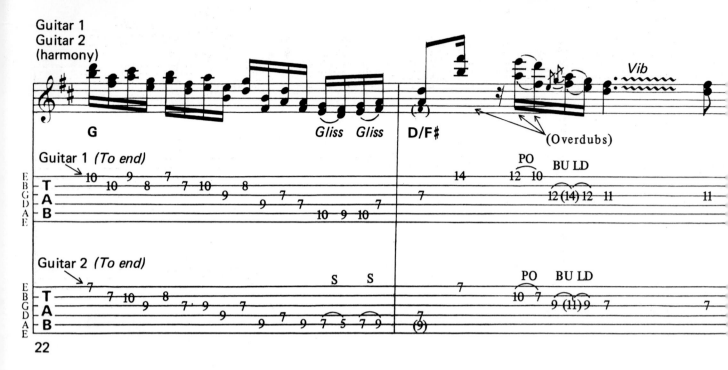

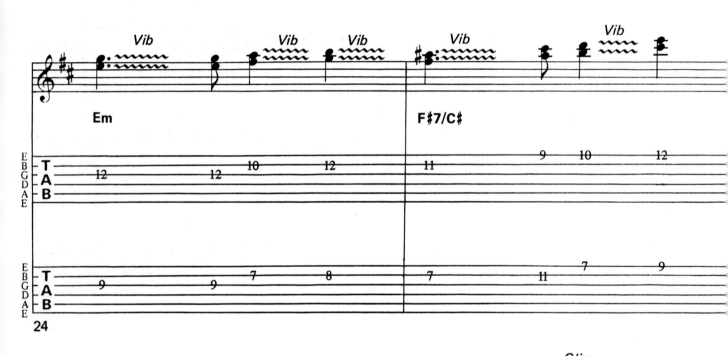

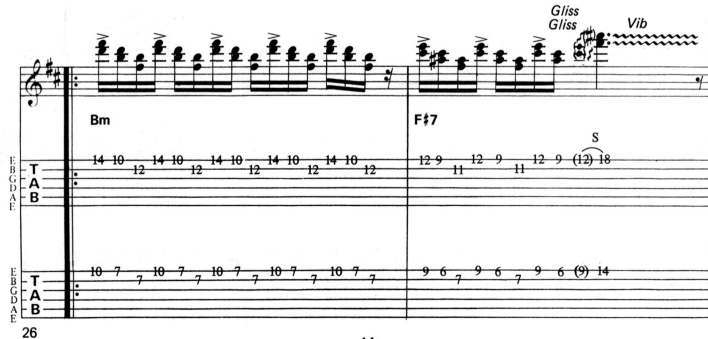

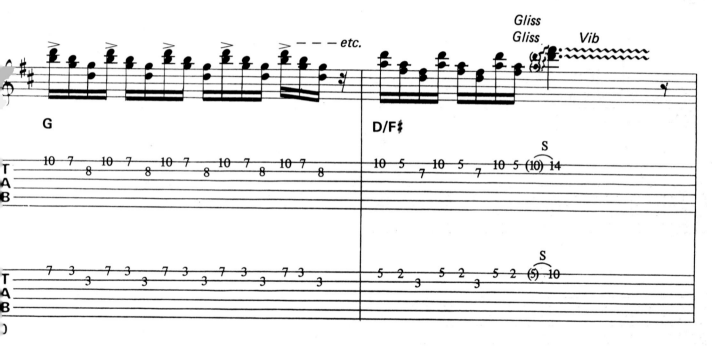

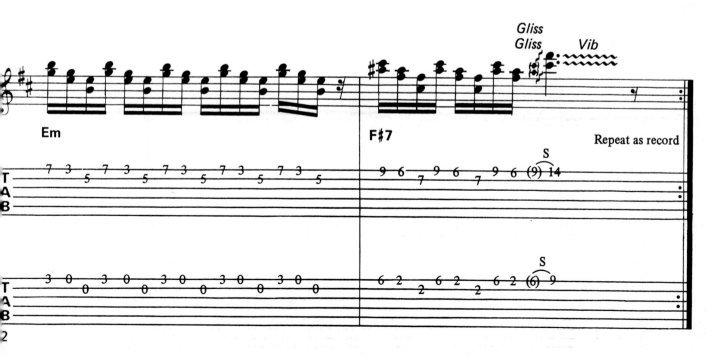

This solo relies fairly heavily on two scale types, the B minor pentatonic:

```
B  D   E  F#  A   B
1  b3  4  5   b7  1
```

and the B aeolian mode/natural minor scale:

```
B  C#  D   E  F#  G   A   B
1  2   b3  4  5   b6  b7  1
```

although there are also a number of occasions where the melody line has been altered to correspond to the accompanying chord progression. One example of this is the A# in bar 3 which, although not featured in either of the aforementioned scales, is the third of the F#7 chord. To find other examples simply compare the accidentals shown in the music notation to the notes in the chords.

There are also some passing note ideas in bars 13 and 15. In bar 13 the melody line descends chromatically from B to G# (the third of the E7 chord) and in bar 15 the melody line ascends chromatically from F# to A.

Joe Walsh starts the solo on a Gibson (probably a Les Paul) and Don Felder comes in later playing a Fender (probably a Strat), although on the transcription I have designated them 'guitar 1' and 'guitar 2. If you intend to play the solo with another guitarist simpy follow the parts as indicated. If you wish to play it on your own, however, I would suggest you follow the top part to the last downbeat of bar 21 (A), then the lower part (guitar 2) to the end of bar 25. After this, return to the upper part (guitar 1) for the remainder of the solo.

In bar 8 all the bends should be played using your first finger, as this will enable you to play the phrase without having to shift position. This also applies to the G-G# bend in bar 5.

The most difficult part of the solo, technically speaking, is probably the arpeggio section in bars 26-33, where you may need to work on some of the stretches and where you will definitely need to take care over the long fourth finger slides!

From the Eagles' album 'Hotel California' (Elektra/Asylum K53051). ©WEA.

46

# PETER FRAMPTON
# STOP

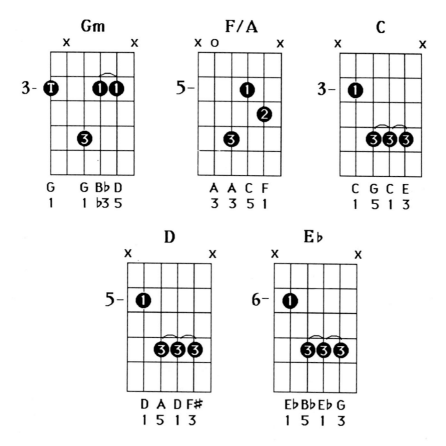

**Gm** — G G Bb D / 1 1 b3 5

**F/A** — A A C F / 3 3 5 1

**C** — C G C E / 1 5 1 3

**D** — D A D F# / 1 5 1 3

**Eb** — Eb Bb Eb G / 1 5 1 3

Moderate ♩ = 118 (Approx)

8va throughout — — — —

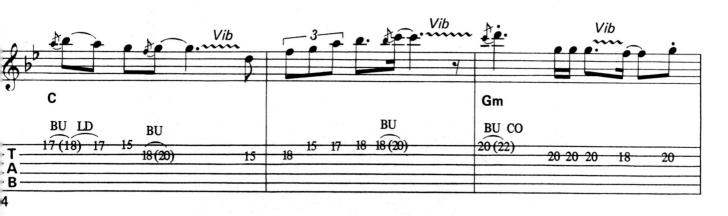

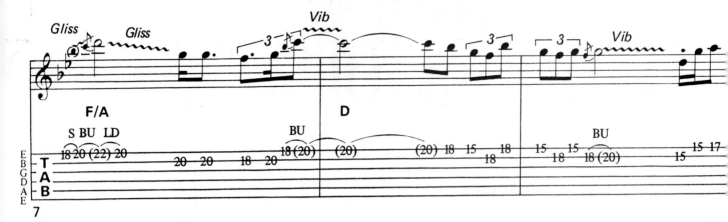

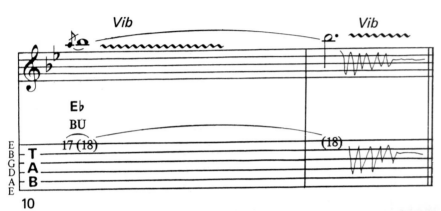

Peter Frampton has always struck me as a very melodic and lyrical player and in this solo, taken from the opening track of his 1986 album 'Premonition', he certainly remains true to form. Melodically, the entire solo is based around the pentatonic scale of G minor which in note selection terms is more or less standard fare:

| G | Bb | C | D | F | G |
|---|----|---|---|---|---|
| 1 | b3 | 4 | 5 | b7 | 1 |

The only notes used which aren't found in the above scale are the two As; the 6th of the C chord in bar 5 and 5th of the D chord in bar 9.

Peter has managed to avoid many of the cliches usually associated with this scale type, and in so doing has ended up with a solo which, although not particularly technical, is certainly very tasteful and fits the mood of the song well.

As this is a very straightforward solo, it shouldn't present any problems, although a couple of areas that may need attention are the phrasing, which should 'swing' and not be as straight as it appears on paper, and the vibrato, which you should try to vary in both speed and width as on the record.

Taken from the Peter Frampton album 'Premonition' (Virgin TCV2365).

# ROBERT FRIPP
# THE NIGHT WATCH

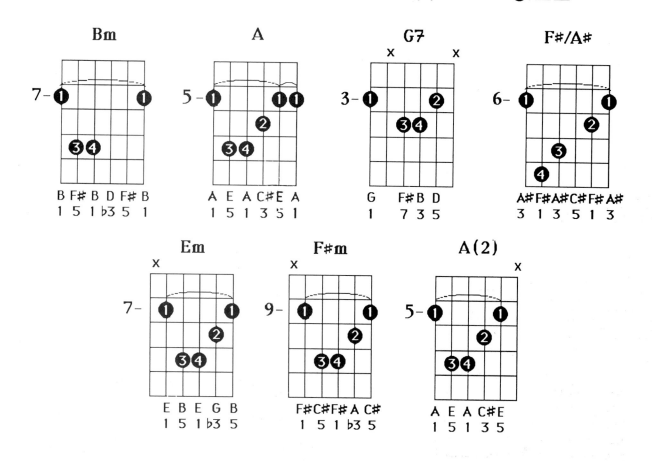

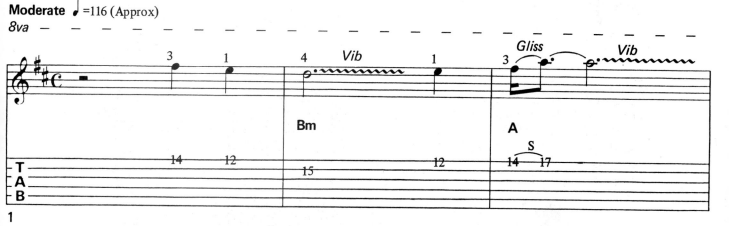

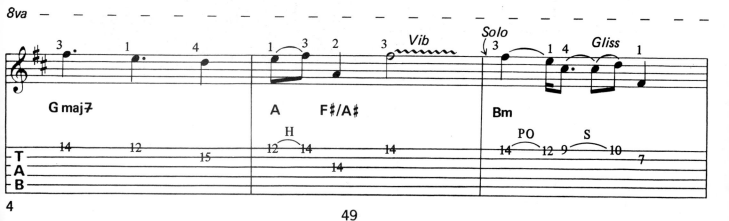

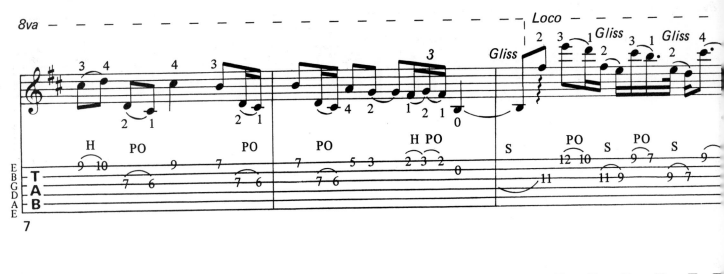

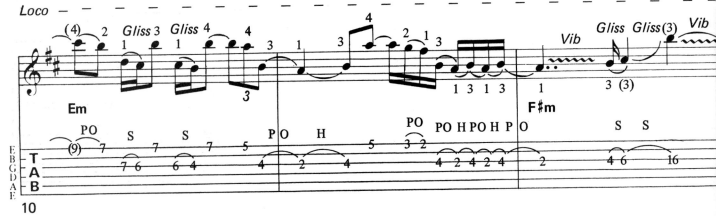

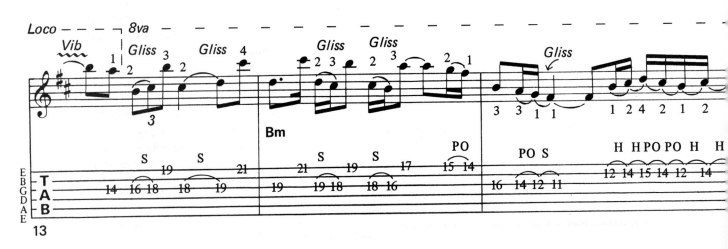

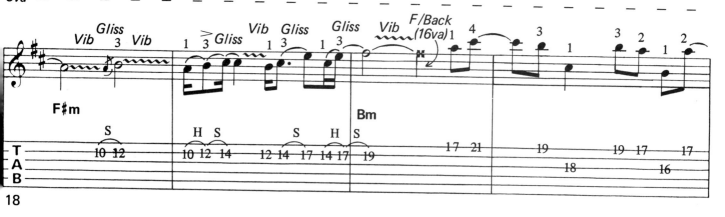

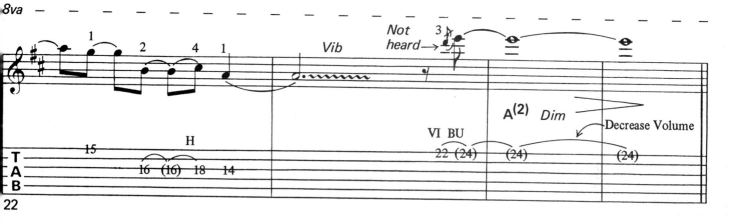

This is based on the B aeolian mode/natural minor scale:

| B | C# | D | E | F# | G | A | B |
|---|----|---|---|----|---|---|---|
| 1 | 2 | b3 | 4 | 5 | b6 | b7 | 1 |

The five bars that precede the solo are part of the melody line that Robert plays behind the vocal, the first three notes of bars 1 and 2 – F#, E and D – falling on the words ". . . for the Wife". Incidentally, for the first bar of the solo, bar 6, I have shown the guitar part that can be heard in the left hand stereo channel.

One of the most interesting aspects of this solo is the frequency with which Robert plays on non adjacent strings, mainly in interval leaps of sixths and sevenths that are combined with pull offs and slides to produce angular phrase ideas. Had these been less rhythmically complex, they would be reminiscent of the kind of playing more usually associated with country guitar styles, but due to the

rhythms and figuration of these phrases, any resemblance is only very slight.

If you are working from the notation and have difficulty coping with the phrasing of bars 15-16, I would strongly recommend that you listen to the record, as this slurred run doesn't sound half as intimidating as it appears on paper.

The symbol VI in the tab for bar 23 stands for 'violining', which means that the note (in this case a bend) must be picked with the volume control off (either on your guitar or, as in Robert's case, with a volume pedal), then without any audible plectrum attack, the volume gradually increased, so the note 'swells' in a smooth manner. If done correctly this will produce an effect vaguely similar to the sound of a bowed violin.

Incidentally, this solo was probably played on Robert Fripp's Gibson Les Paul, Black Beauty.

From the King Crimson album 'Starless And Bible Black' (Polydor 2302/065). Also on the compilation album 'The Young Persons Guide To King Crimson' (Polydor 2612035).

# BILLY GIBBONS
# LEGS

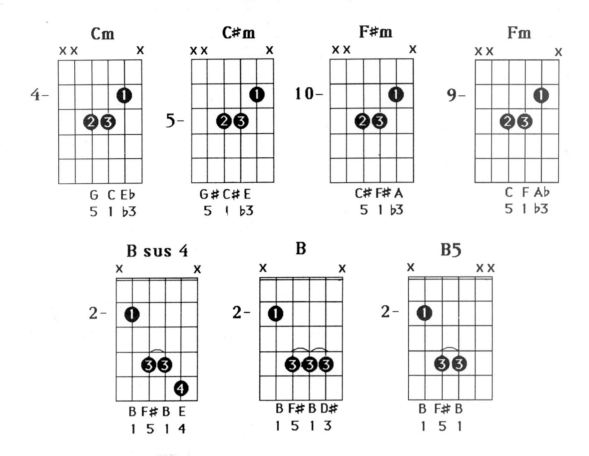

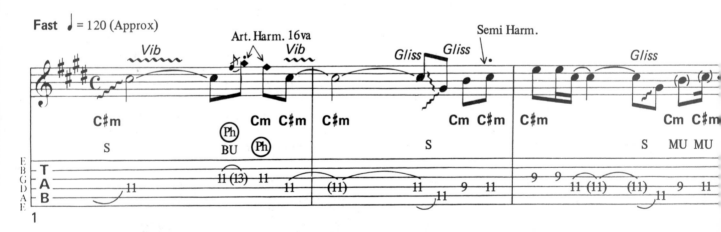

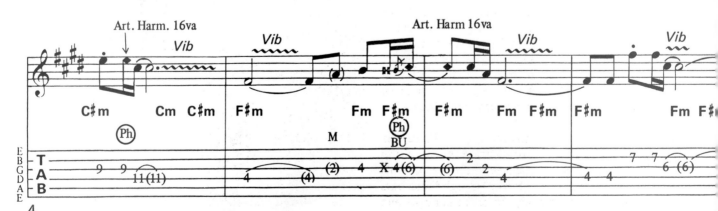

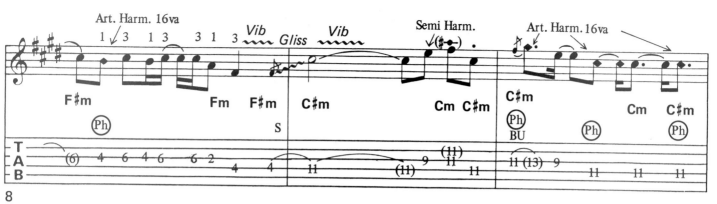

Billy Gibbons based this solo around two scales, the C# minor pentatonic:

C# E F# G# B C#
1 b3 4 5 b7 1

and the F# minor pentatonic:

F# A B C# E F#
1 b3 4 5 b7 1

The only note used which falls outside these two scales is the A# grace note in bar 9.

One of the main features of this solo, and indeed of Billy Gibbons' playing in general, is his use of pinched artificial harmonics, which fall here in bars 1, 4, 5, 8, 10, 11 and 12. They can be produced by catching the string with the flesh of your righthand thumb immediately after picking, approximately 24 frets higher than the fretted fundamental. If performed correctly this will bring out the artificial harmonics sounding two octaves above the fretted fundamental.

On the record, particularly in bars 10-12, the harmonics are a little inconsistent in volume, but as Billy's playing style is characteristically raw this adds to the appeal. In playing through these bars yourself you should apply the same principle and

simply 'dig in' to bring out harmonics wherever possible.

The progression behind the solo is a straight forward I-IV progression in C# minor and the scales used alternate between C# minor pentatonic and F# minor pentatonic in accordance with the underlying changes.

When the solo returns to the rhythm part in bars 15 and 16, the rhythm figures shown are a composite of both parts.

Taken from the ZZ Top album 'Eliminator' ©SBK Songs

53

# DAVID GILMOUR
# ANOTHER BRICK IN THE WALL

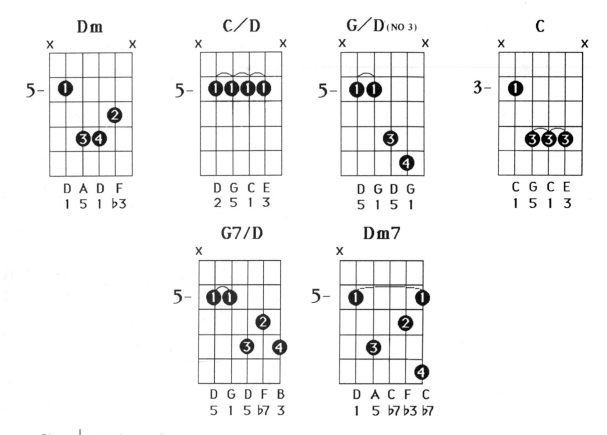

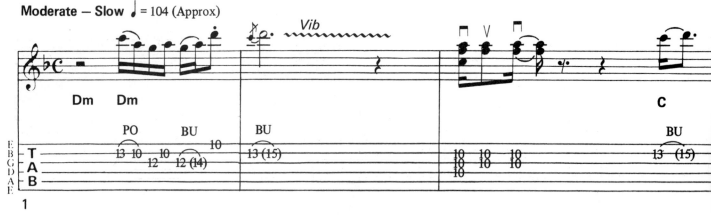

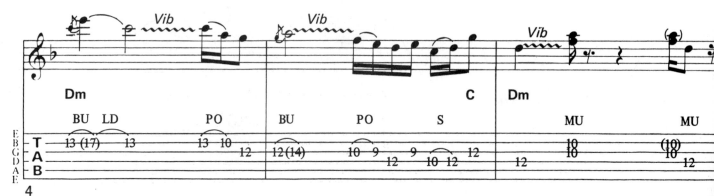

55

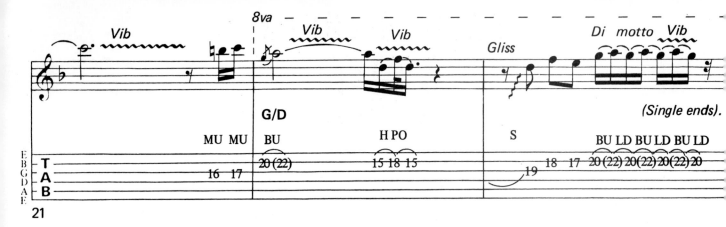

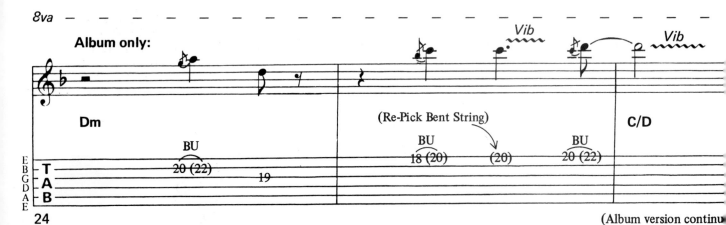

**21**

**24**

(Album version continued for six more bars)

This transcription shows the complete solo from Pink Floyd's hit single, *Another Brick In The Wall*, as well as a couple of phrases from the longer album version (Pink Floyd 'The Wall' Show 411). The scales used include the D minor pentatonic:

| D | F | G | A | C | D |
|---|---|---|---|---|---|
| 1 | b3 | 4 | 5 | b7 | 1 |

and the D Dorian mode:

| D | E | F | G | A | B | C | D |
|---|---|---|---|---|---|---|---|
| 1 | 2 | b3 | 4 | 5 | 6 | b7 | 1 |

*Another Brick In The Wall* is, to my mind, a very good example of Dave Gilmour's playing style; it features tasteful phrasing, subtle dynamics, masterful string bending/vibrato and above all a great sense of 'taste' and 'feel'. Notice, for example, how the spaces that Dave leaves between each melodic statement give the solo a rambling quality, allowing each individual idea 'room to breathe'.

Technically you will need to watch out for some of the string bending, particularly the two tone bend in bar 4, the two stage bend of a tone up to two tones in bar 19, and the rather severe three stage bend of a tone/two tones/two and a half tones in bar 11.

If you feel that your string bending isn't up to scratch, you would be well advised to concentrate on these phrases first, before attempting the whole solo. Also, when you play the phrase in bar 11 you may find that the bend won't sustain for the required amount of time. If this is the case I would

suggest you re-pick the string immediately prior to bending up to the high F, taking care to make it sound as smooth as possible.

# DAVID GILMOUR
# TIME

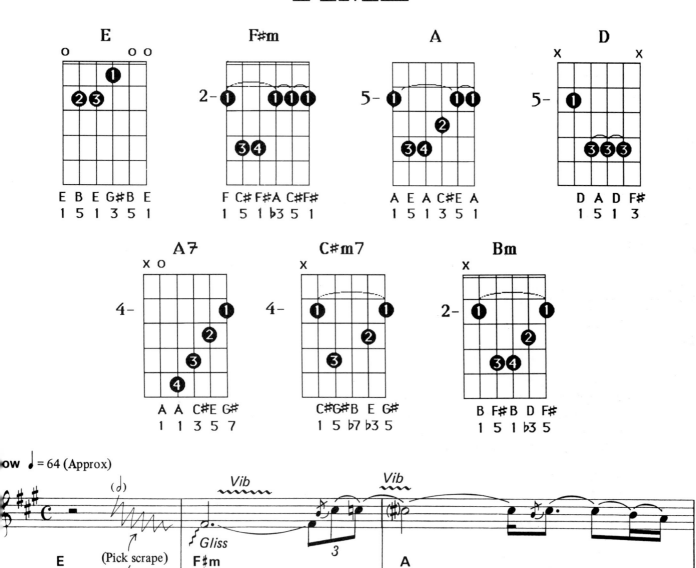

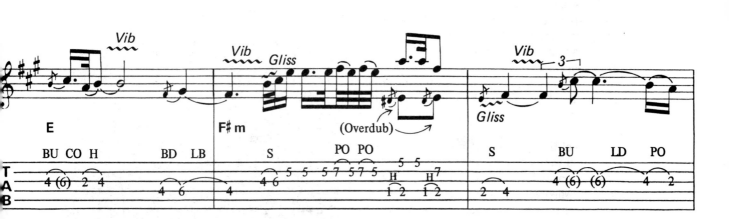

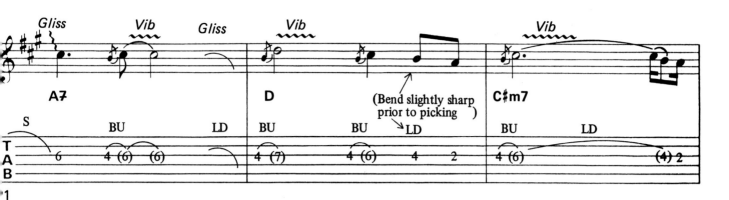

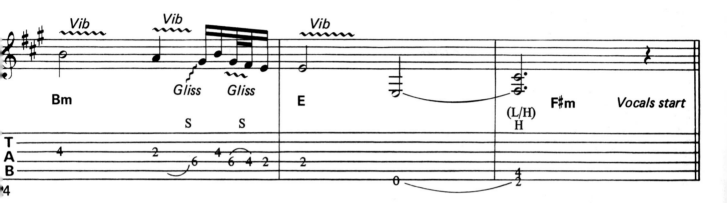

*Time* is taken from Pink Floyd's immensely successful album, 'Dark Side Of The Moon'. David Gilmour's solo on the track uses a combination of three scale types, namely the F# minor pentatonic:

| F# | A | B | C# | E | F# |
|----|-----|---|----|---|----|
| 1 | b3 | 4 | 5 | b7 | 1 |

the F# blues scale

| F# | A | B | C | C# | E | F# |
|----|-----|---|---|----|---|----|
| 1 | b3 | 4 | b5 | 5 | b7 | 1 |

and the F# aeolian mode/natural minor scale:

| F# | G# | A | B | C# | D | E | F# |
|----|-----|---|---|----|---|---|----|
| 1 | 2 | b3 | 4 | 5 | b6 | b7 | 1 |

Two important facets of the sound David achieves in this solo are his use of a Fender Strat coupled with delay' (probably from an analogue device).

Throughout the piece you will need to pay close attention to the pitching of bends and the width of vibrato. The bends vary in size from a semi-tone to a tone and a half, and on the whole are either held for long periods of time, or let down to specific pitches. The vibrato can be produced by either normal left hand techniques, or by the tremolo arm, and it is essential that you listen to the record to hear the amount of variation produced.

In addition to the scales mentioned above, some arpeggio ideas are used: F# minor, first triplet bar 10; E major, beats 3-4 bar 16; and D major 6 sus 4, bar 18. On paper the phrasing appears to be quite complex, however, it is a very lyrical solo and after listening to the phrasing should be easy to memorise.

Finally, on the last beat of bar 5 there is an overdubbed guitar part, which enters before the completion of the original phrase. As it is impossible to play both parts simultaneously, I would suggest you use your discretion in deciding which part to follow.

Taken from the Pink Floyd album 'Dark Side Of The Moon' (Harvest SHVL 804).
©Pink Floyd Publ.

# PETER GREEN
# NEED YOUR LOVE SO BAD

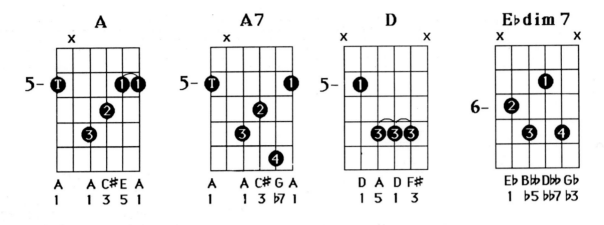

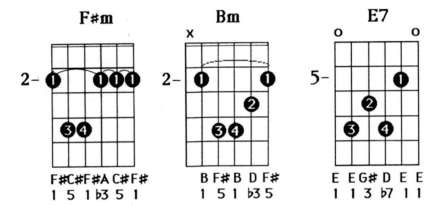

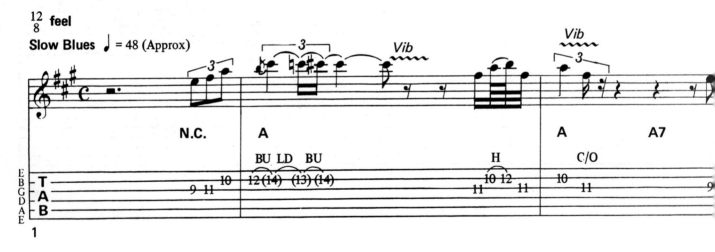

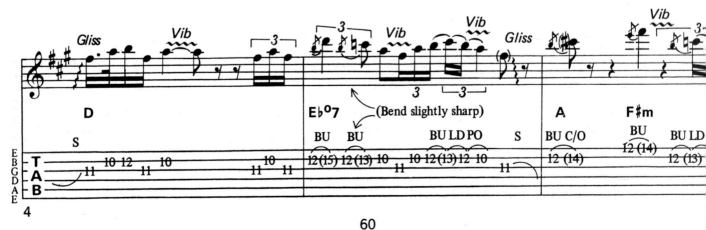

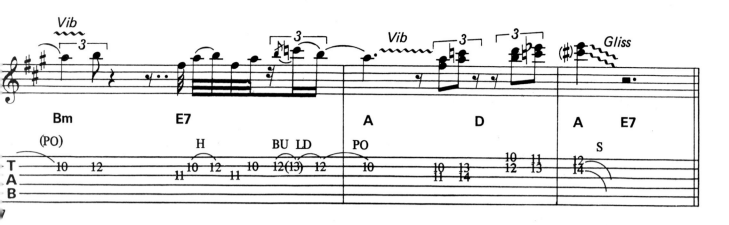

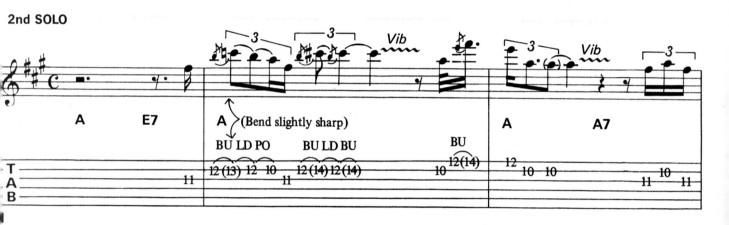

**2nd SOLO**

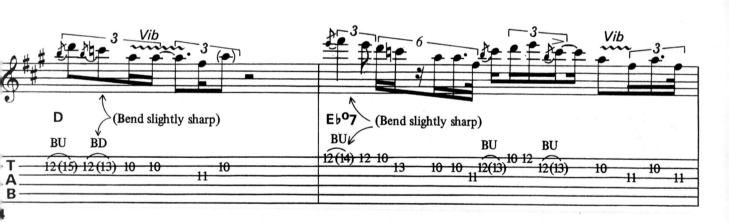

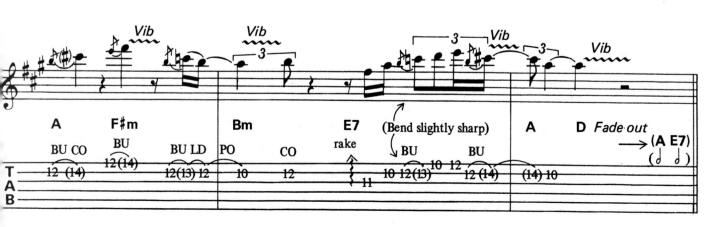

Both solos from *Need Your Love So Bad* are played over an eight bar blues progression although, unlike many similar blues chord sequences, it doesn't rely solely on chords I (A A7) IV (D) and V (E7), but also uses a diminished 7th chord (Eb dim 7, bar 5) and two minor chords (F#m, bar 6, Bm, bar 7).

Both solos are based around the hybrid A major/minor pentatonic scale:

| A | B | C | C# | D | E | F# | G | A |
|---|---|---|----|---|---|----|---|---|
| 1 | 2 | b3 | 3 | 4 | 5 | 6 | b7 | 1 |

The only note 'outside' this scale type is the b5 (Eb) in bar 8 of the first solo.

Peter Green is a player with great affinity and 'feel' for soulful, lyrical blues playing. When this type of playing is transcribed it often appears more rythmically complex than it actually sounds. If you have any problem coping with the phrasing I would suggest you work on both solos in close conjunction with the record.

Throughout each solo there is a good deal of string bending which should be performed as accurately as possible, paying particular attention to the areas where you need to overbend slightly in order to produce the required 'bluesy' quartertone effects.

Two further important facets of Peter's playing are his control over dynamics and vibrato, both of which are well represented in these solos so, to produce a convincing performance, it is vital that close attention is paid to these areas.

From the Fleetwood Mac compilation album 'Fleetwood Mac' Greatest Hits' (CBS 69011). ©CBS/SBK Songs.

# GEORGE HARRISON
# LET IT BE

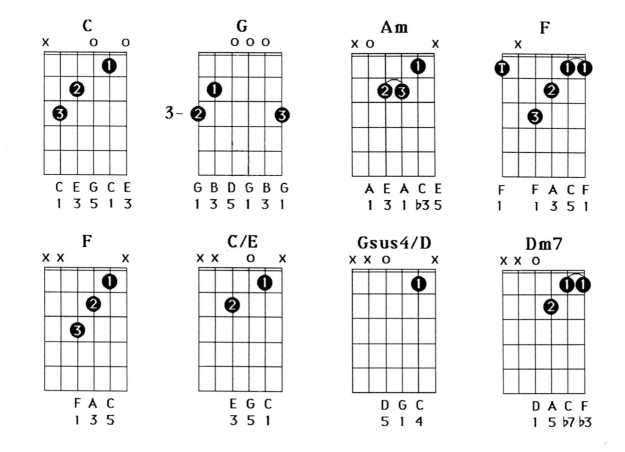

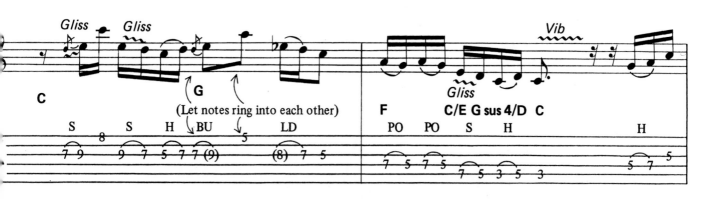

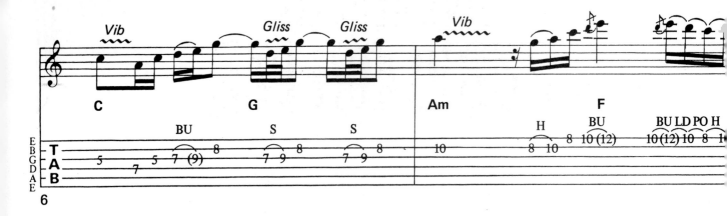

George Harrison's solo on *Let It Be* was probably composed rather than improvised, and as such is a good example of his melodious and precise approach to soloing.

Only one scale type is used for the entire solo, the C major pentatonic:

C D E G A C
1 2 3 5 6 1

Technically, it is a very straightforward solo, although the slides in bars 1, 4 (beat 2), 5 and 7 may need close attention. They should all be phrased metrically as indicated by the notation and in bars 2 and 4 should be treated as grace notes.

Much of the phrasing is based on a question/answer format with most of the phrases concluding on either chord tones or common suspensions/additions. There is one notable exception to this, however, in bar 7 where the D-E bend on the third beat forms an interval of a compound major 7th against the accompanying F chord.

During the sessions for the 'Let It Be' album George Harrison used a Gibson Les Paul, a Fender Telecaster and a Fender amp.

Finally, please remember the solo on the single of *Let It Be* is different to the album version transcribed here.

From The Beatles album 'Let It Be' (EMI/Apple TC-PCS 7096)
©1970 Northern Songs Ltd.

# JIMI HENDRIX
# PURPLE HAZE

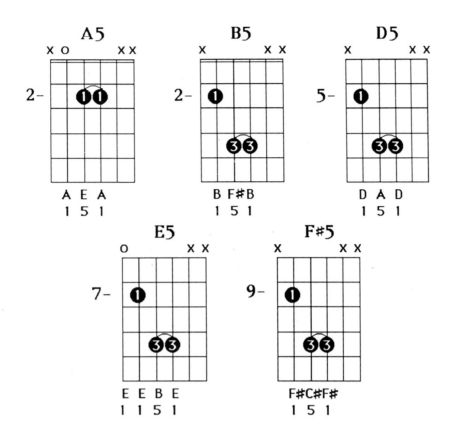

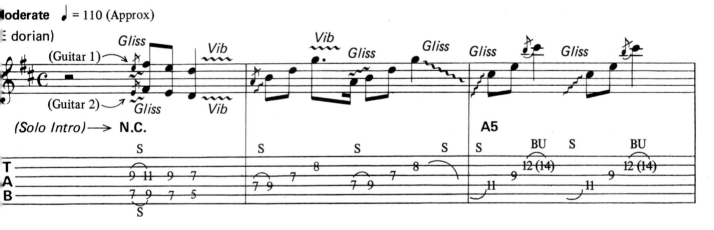

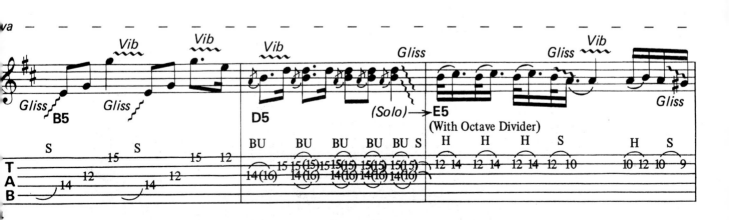

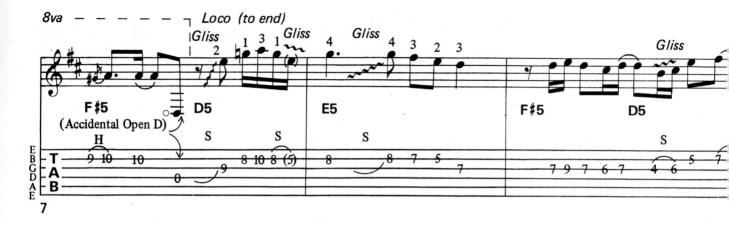
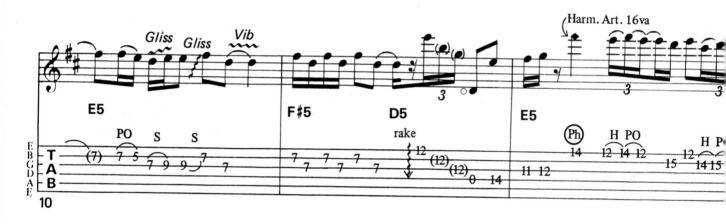
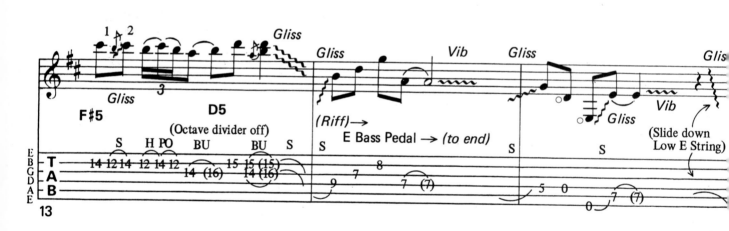
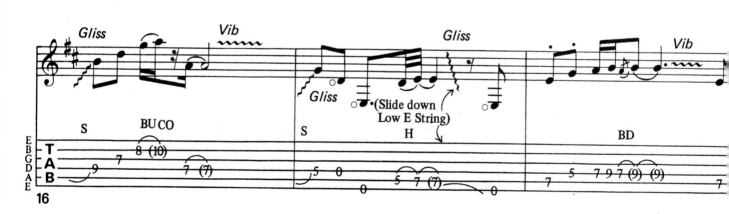

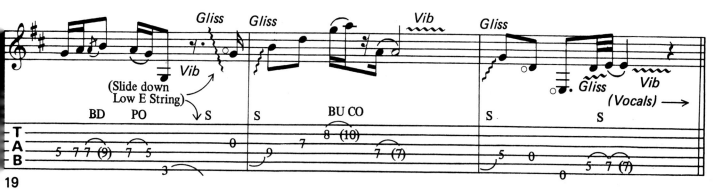

**19**

*Purple Haze* is certainly one of the tracks most commonly associated with this legendary guitarist and the transcription here shows the bridge section (bars 1-5), the solo (bars 6-13) and the variation on the main riff that Jimi played to lead back to the song (bars 13-21). Throughout all three sections Jimi uses one scale type, the E Dorian mode:

```
E  F#  G   A  B  C#  D   E
1  2   b3  4  5  6   b7  1
```

The only other notes used, which don't appear in the above scale type, are the G#s in bars 6 and 7. G# is the major third of the accompanying E chord (bar 6), and the 9th of the F# chord (bar 7).

In the first bar of the bridge section Jimi plays a descending three note fill using octaves. As you play this you should damp the D string with the underside of whichever finger you use to play the notes on the A string.

Bars 2-4 contain an ascending series of triadic arpeggio ideas which outline the G major chord in bar 2, A minor (no root) in bar 3 and Em/B in bar 4.

Jimi modified his sound for the solo by using an octave divider. This was probably an early or even a prototype version of the effect, as it sounds markedly different to the effect available nowadays.

Technically there are some fairly unusual fingerings, especially in bars 9 and 12, but as the solo is played at a fairly moderate pace they shouldn't prove too difficult to come to terms with.

The main riff played at the end of the solo is essentially a variation of the one that appears during the intro to the song. It still contains the same interesting open string ideas but the phrasing is different, particularly during the question/answer idea in bars 18-19.

From the Jimi Hendrix compilation album 'The Essential Jimi Hendrix' (Polydor 2612 034). (Originally recorded on 'Are You Experienced' ©Phonogram.

# JIMI HENDRIX
# LITTLE WING

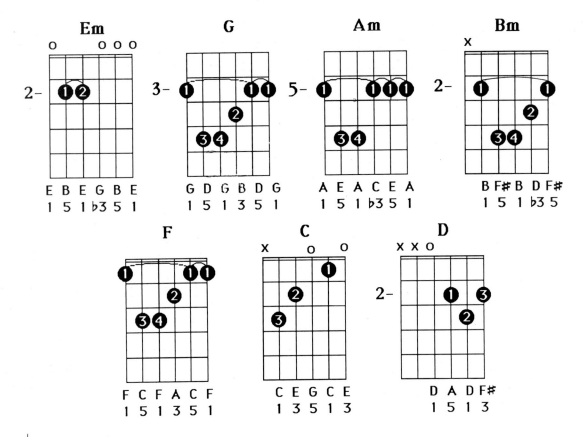

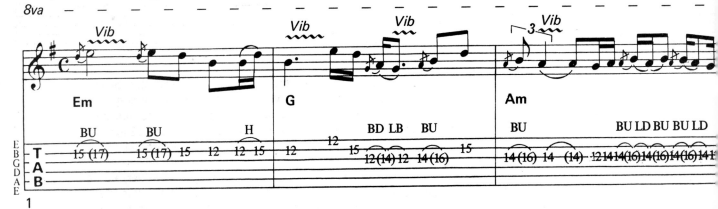

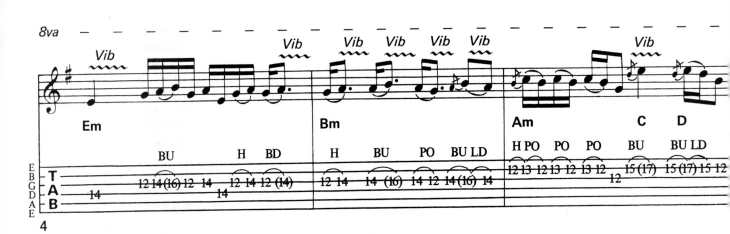

68

The track *Little Wing* originally appeared on Jimi's second album 'Axis Bold As Love' and to my mind it's one of the most impressive songs he ever recorded. The introduction is stunning and in common with the entire vocal accompaniment, contains examples of some of his most tasteful and innovative chordal playing. The solo transcribed here is a typical example of the soulful side of his playing style.

Analysed in terms of scales it can be seen as using three different scale types, namely the E minor pentatonic:

```
E  G  A  B  D  E
1  b3 4  5  b7 1
```

E aeolian mode/natural minor scale:

```
E  F#  G  A  B  C  D  E
1  2   b3 4  5  b6 b7 1  (bars 8-9)
```

and the E phrygian mode

```
E  F  G  A  B  C  D  E
1  b2 b3 4  5  b6 b7 1  (bar 7)
```

Bars 1-6 feature some fairly standard bluesy minor pentatonic phrases. Notice during this section how, as well as using chord tones, Jimi also shows a fondness for notes b6, b7, 9 and 11 against minor chords and notes 6 and 9 against major chords.

In bars 7-10 Jimi uses a chordal rather than a linear approach. As you play through this it is vitally important that all the bends are allowed to reach the correct pitches, and that they ring into each other wherever possible. As you play the E minor triad in bar 10, the S + TA LD symbols above the tab indicate that you should simultaneously slide down the neck (towards the nut) and depress the tremolo arm.

The closing four bars (bars 11-14) return to minor pentatonic based ideas. Notice how chord tones are again used here to outline and accent the changes and how lyrical and inventive the phrasing is.

Jimi played this solo on a Fender Stratocaster. To produce the phasing effect the signal was routed through the Leslie speaker of an organ.

From the Jimi Hendrix compilation album 'Jimi Hendrix' (Polydor 2343 080). Originally recorded on the album 'Axis: Bold As Love'. ©Polydor.

69

# ALLAN HOLDSWORTH
# IN THE MYSTERY

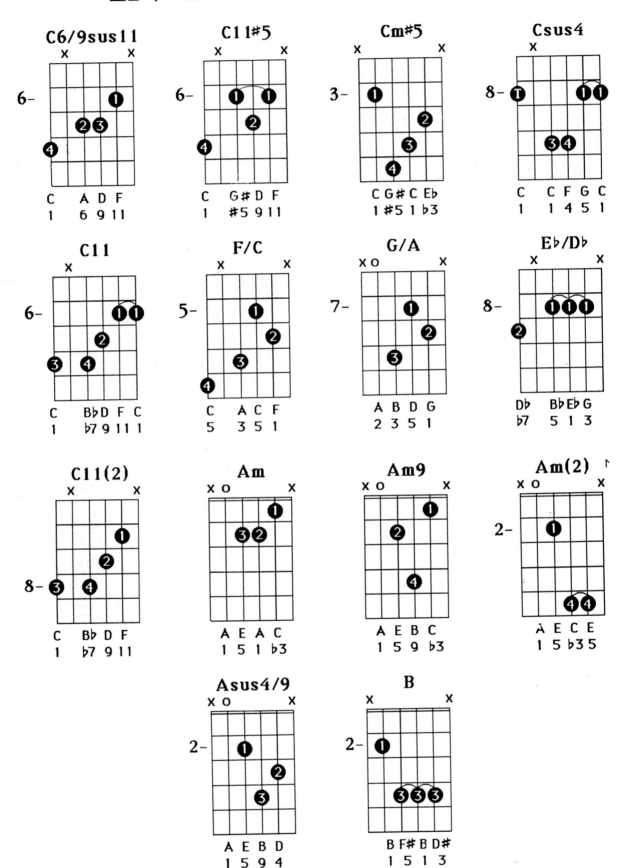

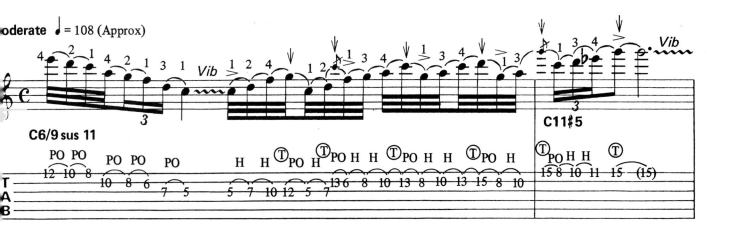

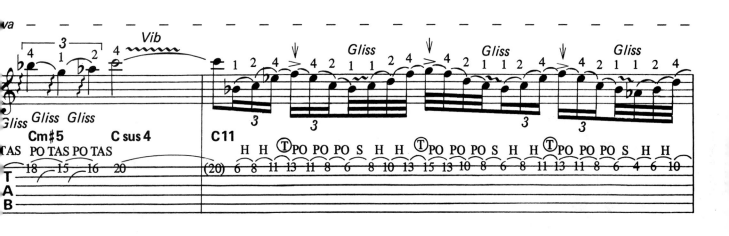

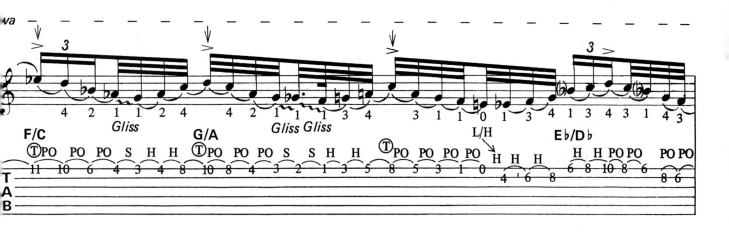

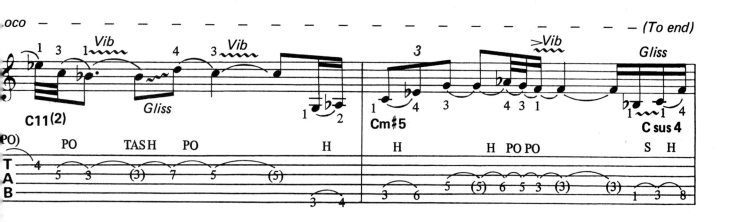

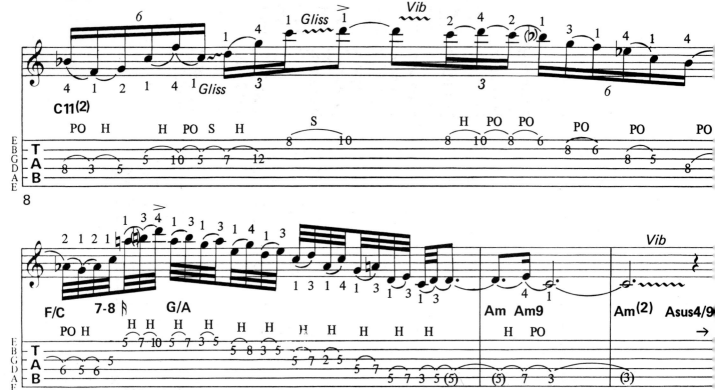

Allan Holdsworth is undoubtedly one of the world's most musically and technically inspiring guitarists. As is generally the case with great innovators, he has a sound and approach which are instantly recognisable as his own. His solos are any transcriber's nightmare, not necessarily because of the number of notes he plays, but because of the problems involved in working out how he physically manages to play them! This solo is taken from his widely acclaimed 'Metal Fatigue' album and although it isn't very long, it does give a good insight into Allan's unique style.

The opening phrase (beats 1-2 of bar 1) is a slurred run which uses exactly the same notes as those normally found in the full arpeggio of the accompanying C6/9 sus 11 chord:

C  E  G  A  D  F
1  3  5  6  9  11

Analysed in terms of scales this arpeggio could be viewed as C major, with an omitted seventh degree:

C  D  E  F  G  A  C
1  2  3  4  5  6  1

The second phrase is a two hand tapping idea and uses the same scale, only this time with the addition of a minor third (Eb b10th). Notice as you play through it, that the second tapped note appears only as a grace note and as such doesn't have a particularly audible melodic function.

Bar 3 contains a simple four note motif. As you play each note of this, the tremolo arm should be depressed slightly, then released, to sound vaguely similar to a conventional left hand slide.

The next phrase, which runs from the first up-beat of bar 4 through to the end of bar 6, is another idea which utilises two hand tapping. This time, however, it is used in combination with left hand slides producing a run that begins by seamlessly ascending and descending the length of the top E string. It is finally rounded off by slurring ideas, which cross the B, E and G strings. As you work

through this watch out for some of the left hand stretches, and as you cross strings on the third up-beat of bar 5 you should play the hammer on with the left hand only – the string should not be picked. As many of the notes in this run are 'outside' the accompanying harmony, you would be well advised to compare the notes in the melody line to those in the chords, taking careful note of the tensions involved.

The run which begins on the second sixteenth note/third beat of bar 7 and ends on the third beat of bar 8 is, to my mind, the most difficult section in terms of left hand stretches. If you are unused to stretches of this size I would suggest you work at building up your technique before attempting this phrase.

The final phrase in bars 9-10 uses the A minor pentatonic scale:

A  C  D  E  G  A
1  b3  4  5  b7  1

in combination with extremely fast hammer ons and position shifts. The fingering given for this represents the only feasible way I could work out to perform the run. However, if you find it impractical or awkward I would suggest you work out an alternative fingering to suit your own preference.

One final point to bear in mind as you work through this solo is that whereas most guitarists use a plucking motion with their left hand for pull offs, Allan has often stated that he uses more of a 'lift off' technique. This, he claims, alleviates the familiar 'plucking' sound that normally accompanies pull offs and therefore results in a far more legato effect. In addition, Allan's guitars are fitted with .008 gauge Ernie Ball strings and all have wide necks with as low a string action as possible!

From the Allan Holdsworth album 'Metal Fatigue' (Enigma 72002-1).
©1985 Enigma Records

# PAUL KOSSOFF
# ALL RIGHT NOW

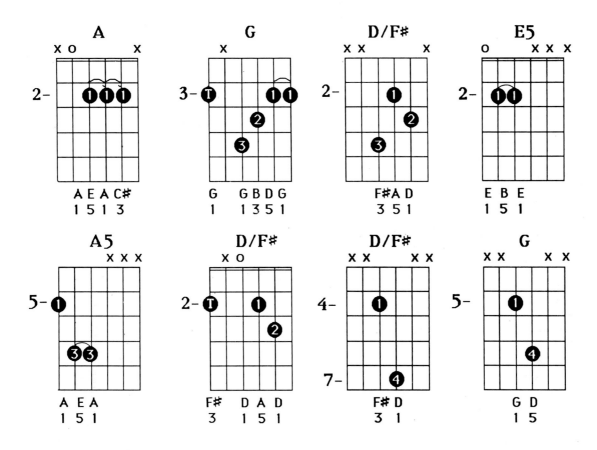

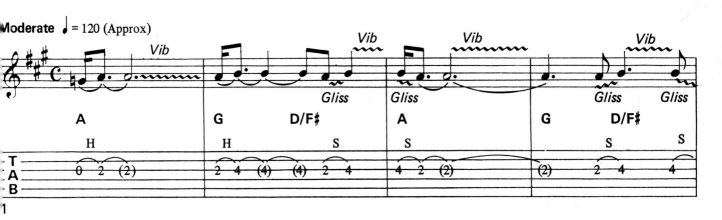

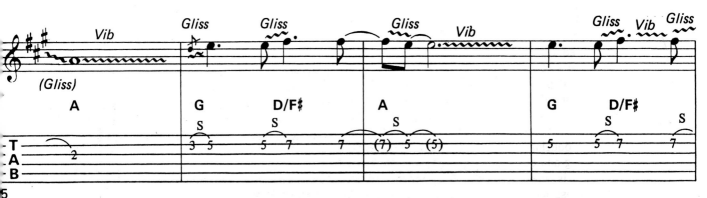

74

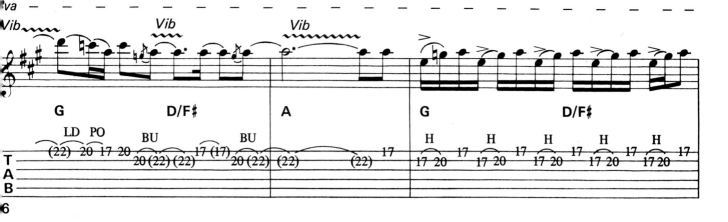

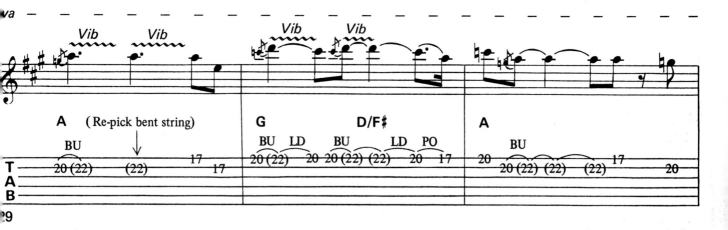

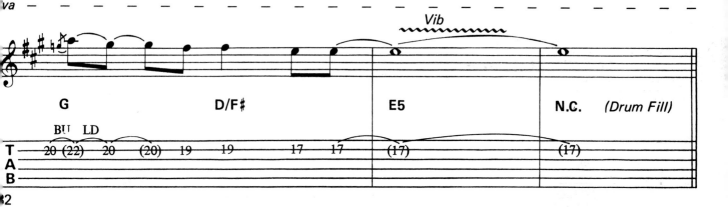

Paul Kossoff's solo on this track must be one of the best known and most popular 70's British rock guitar solos. It is an excellent example of a solo which gradually builds up from a very sparse opening low down the neck, to an exciting 'wailing' finish at the top of the neck.

In terms of scales it is fairly straightforward, using the hybrid major/minor pentatonic throughout:

| A | B | C | C# | D | E | F# | G | A |
|---|---|---|---|---|---|---|---|---|
| 1 | 2 | b3 | 3 | 4 | 5 | 6 | b7 | 1 |

In the opening 9 bars Paul plays some very tasteful question/answer phrases, in which he shows a strong preference for sustaining roots, thirds and sixths against the accompanying major chords.

To play the phrases in bar 10 correctly you

should ensure that you sustain the high A for the correct duration (as indicated in the notation). Failure to do this will alter the sound of the idea quite dramatically.

Bars 14, 16, 24 and 28 all contain examples of 3 against 4 polyrhythms. In bars 14 and 16 these all start on up beats, and in bars 24 and 28 on down beats. Watch out for the difference and take care to accent the notes as indicated above the music notation.

The remaining sections shouldn't present any undue problems, although care should be taken to ensure that the bends all reach the correct pitches and that the vibrato 'sings' in the manner displayed on the record.

From the Free single *Alright Now* (Island WIP 6082) ©1970 Island Records Ltd.

# STEVE LUKATHER
# ROSANNA

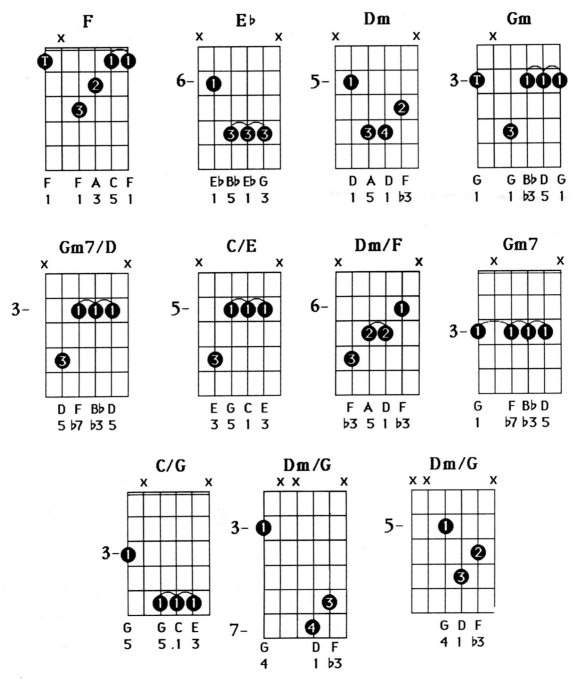

1st SOLO

Moderate ♩ = 84 (Approx)

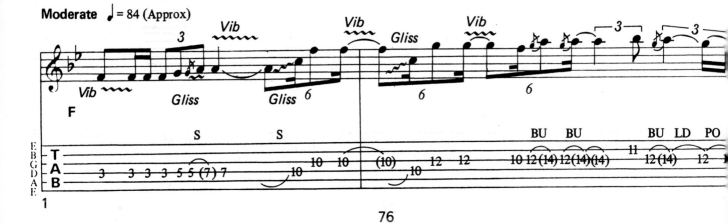

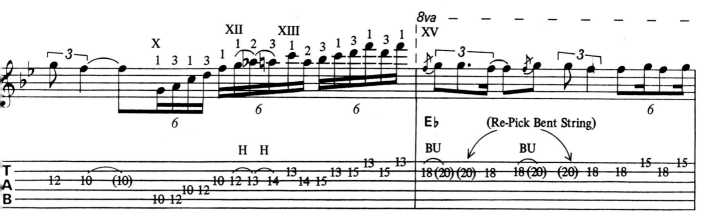

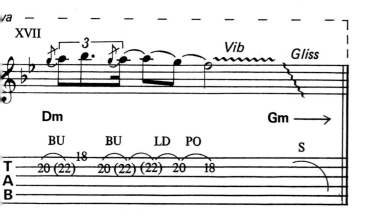

**2ND SOLO**

**Very Fast** ♩ = 168 (Approx)

**G dorian**

**G minor Chord Pattern throughout**
see notes

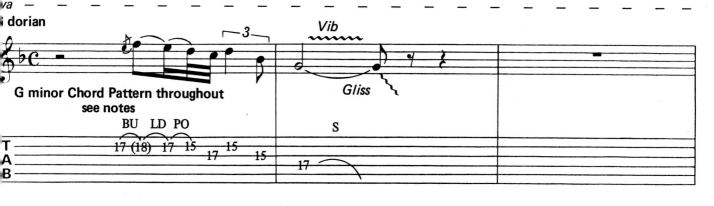

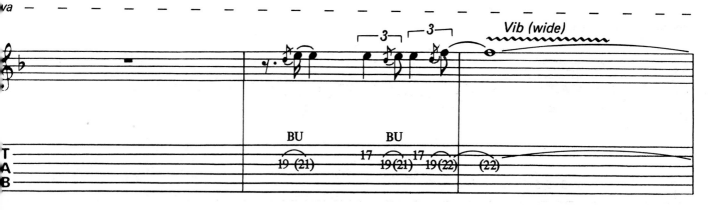

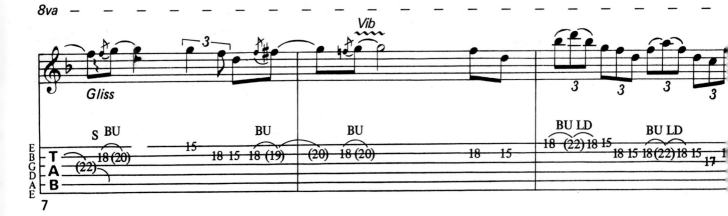

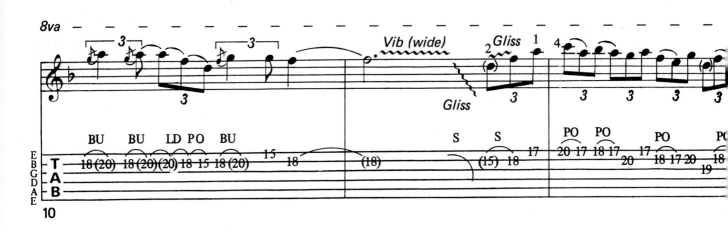

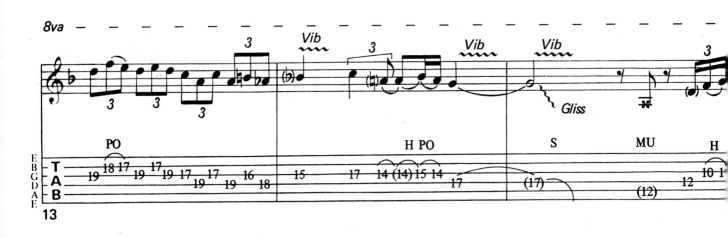

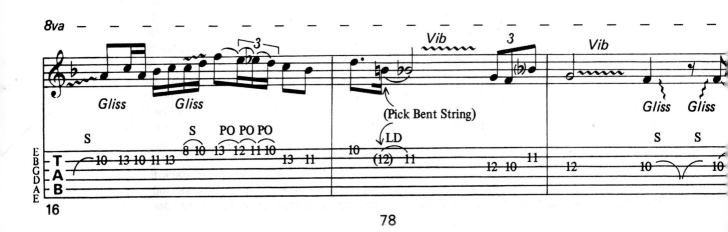

**AST LINE**

As well as being one of the world's most sought after session musicians, Steve Lukather is also a founder member of the band Toto. Both solos transcribed here are taken from one of the band's most successful and best known tracks which, in addition to appearing as the opening track on their album 'Toto IV', was a massive hit single.

The first solo is very tasteful and well constructed. Apart from the passing notes in bar 3 it uses the F mixolydian mode throughout:

| F | G | A | Bb | C | D | Eb | F |
|---|---|---|----|---|---|----|---|
| 1 | 2 | 3 | 4  | 5 | 6 | b7 | 1 |

The opening two bars of this solo feature an ascending idea which makes good use of chord tones to outline the accompanying F chord. This is followed in bar 3 by another ascending phrase which uses the 'blue note' b3 (Ab) to add a little chromatic colour to the idea. The final two bars feature phrases played high up the neck, for which Steve uses string bending to good effect by bending into the major third of the Eb chord (G) and the fifth of the D minor chord (A). Notice how the solo ends on F, the minor third of D minor, which is the same as the first note of this solo only two octaves higher.

When Toto were recording this track the band played 'live' in the studio and the second solo on the track came about as the result of a spontaneous 'jam' at the end of the song. If this is true, and I see no reason to doubt it, then this solo really does demonstrate how awesome a player Steve is. Throughout the solo his superb control over phrasing, vibrato and feel are well exhibited and provide models which are well worth aspiring to.

It is based around three scale types, the G dorian mode:

| G | A | Bb | C | D | E | F | G |
|---|---|----|---|---|---|---|---|
| 1 | 2 | b3 | 4 | 5 | 6 | b7 | 1 |

the G minor pentatonic scale:

| G | Bb | C | D | F | G |
|---|----|---|---|---|---|
| 1 | b3 | 4 | 5 | b7 | 1 |

and the G blues scale:

| G | Bb | C | Db | D | F | G |
|---|----|---|----|---|---|---|
| 1 | b3 | 4 | b5 | 5 | b7 | 1 |

The first three phrases in bars 1-2, 5-6 and 7-8 are fairly straightforward blues based ideas. The following phrase in bars 9-10 contains some interesting string bending, however. As you play though this you will need to take care to ensure that both the E and B string bends in bar 9 reach the correct pitches. In both cases the bends are of a major third.

Bars 11-14 feature a descending triplet figure that uses the G dorian mode. As well as this scale form a couple of chromatic passing notes are also used – B and Ab, bar 13. These are some of Steve's favourite devices and they work well in this kind of phrase, introducing a little tension into the run, making it sound more colourful than a normal 'straight' scale based idea.

The run in bars 15-18 contains another example of chromaticism. Here the chromatic section is the line which descends from F to D on the third beat of bar 16. Bar 19 features a triplet phrase which necessitates quite a large left hand stretch in order to play the first series of notes. Throughout this passage you should leave your left hand first finger on the F (10th fret, G string).

The phrasing for the unison bend ideas in bars 22-24 may prove difficult to read and will probably need to be worked on in conjunction with the record.

The final three bars (25-26) feature a very fast blues scale passage. This will probably sound more fluid if it is memorised first and then slowly built up to speed over a period of time.

The accompanying chord progression of Gm7, C/G, Dm/G, C/G, Gm7 and C/G should be phrased in the same way as the keyboard chords on the record. If you use the alternative progression, Gm7/D, C/E, Dm/F, you should bear in mind that the root notes of each chord correspond to the bass player's bass line.

From the Toto album 'Toto IV' (CBS 85529). ©CBS/SBK Songs.

# YNGWIE MALMSTEEN
# DISCIPLES OF HELL/ AS ABOVE SO BELOW

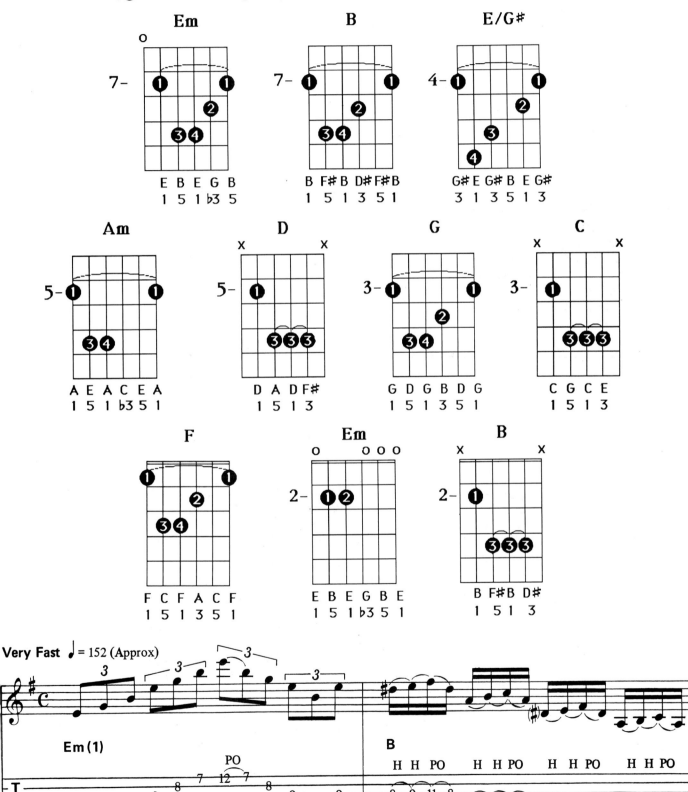

82

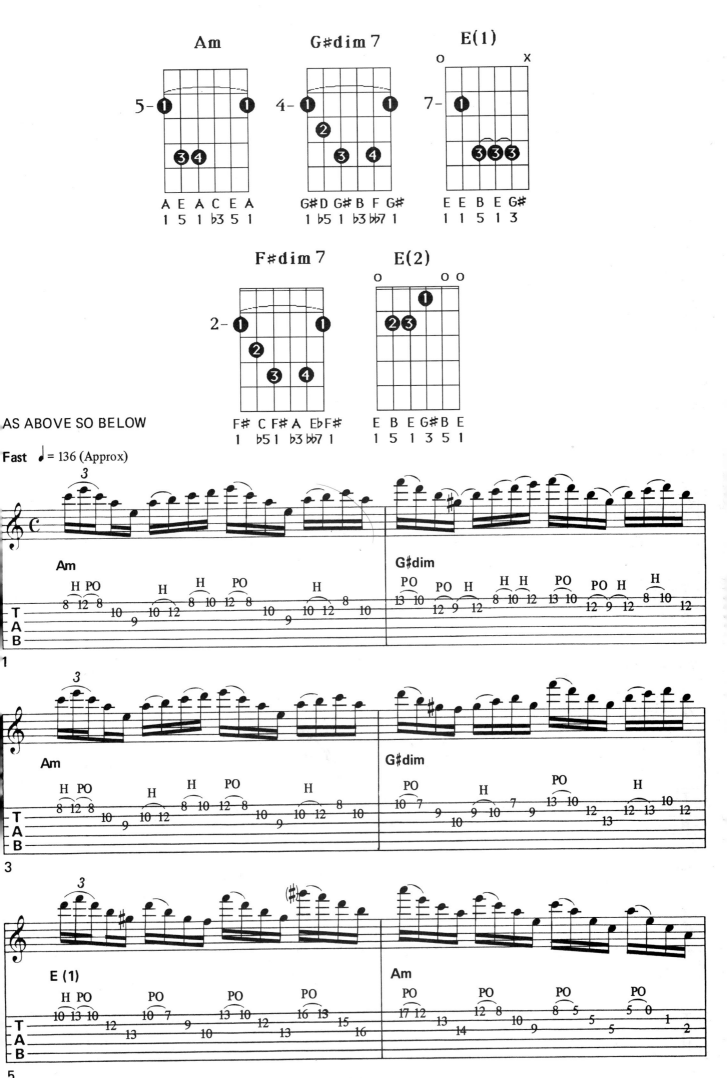

AS ABOVE SO BELOW

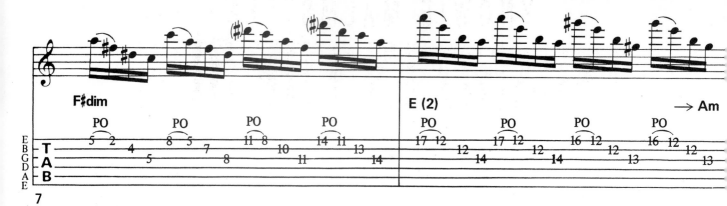

F#dim

E (2)                                                    → Am

7

Although these excerpts from *Disciples Of Hell* and *As Above So Below* are the introductions to two separate tracks, we will look at them together here.

Two scale types are used for *Disciples Of Hell*, namely the E harmonic minor scale:

E  F#  G  A  B  C  D#  E
1  2   b3 4  5  6  7   1

and the E Spanish phrygian/harmonic minor, mixolydian mode:

E  F  G#  A  B  C  D  E
1  b2 3   4  5  b6 b7 1

*As Above So Below* only uses the A harmonic minor scale:

A  B  C  D  E  F  G#  A
1  2  b3 4  5  b6 7   1

As both these intros are arpeggio based, the scales above represent the probable sources of the arpeggios. In fact, both pieces feature a great deal of Yngwie's fast arpeggio and slurring ideas, which are both instantly recognisable 'trademarks' of his virtuosic and classically influenced playing style. To play them at the correct speed you will need a very dexterous and agile left hand, with good control over fast position shifts, slurring, stretching and your fourth finger. If you aren't used to such technically demanding work, or are unfamiliar with fast arpeggio playing, I suggest you look upon both pieces as technical studies and work on them slowly – one bar at a time if necessary – with the correct speed as a long-term objective.

Bar 1 of *Disciples Of Hell*, and the first two beats of bar 3 (triplets), can be played using either glide strokes or, for better articulation, alternate picking (starting with a downstroke).

In bars 2 and 4 some of the notes are picked (tremolo picking) whilst being slurred. Both bars can be played using slurs only (as indicated), and as the picked notes are a little inconsistent, I would suggest you listen closely to the record. Use your own discretion to decide which technique to use.

Some of the arpeggios used (E major, F major) can be seen as being derived from a scale called the Spanish phrygian (see above). This scale is the same as the mixolydian mode of a harmonic minor scale, or a harmonic minor scale starting from its fifth note. In this case, the E Spanish phrygian contains the same notes as the harmonic minor scale of A – A B C D E F G# A – the only difference being that the Spanish phrygian starts on the fifth note, E.

In the second intro, *As Above, So Below*, bar 2 can be re-fingered and played keeping your hand in the tenth position (index finger on the tenth fret). You may find this a little awkward, but it does alleviate the difficulty caused by the position shifts.

Make sure the open strings don't ring during changes in hand position, particularly when playing the ascending diminished arpeggio in bar 7. This should be avoided by muting any offending strings with your right hand palm.

The accompanying chord voicings correspond to the harmony implied by the bass line and not by the guitar arpeggios; if you compare the two you should have little problem noticing where the melody line is tense in relation to the chords.

*Disciples Of Hell* was taken from the album 'Marching Out' (Polydor 825733-1). *As Above So Below* was taken from the album 'Yngwie Malmsteen's Rising Force' (Polydor 825324-1). ©1984/1985 Unichappell Music Inc/De Novo. Reproduced by permision of Intersong Music Ltd and International Music Publications Ltd.

# YNGWIE MALMSTEEN
# ISLAND IN THE SUN

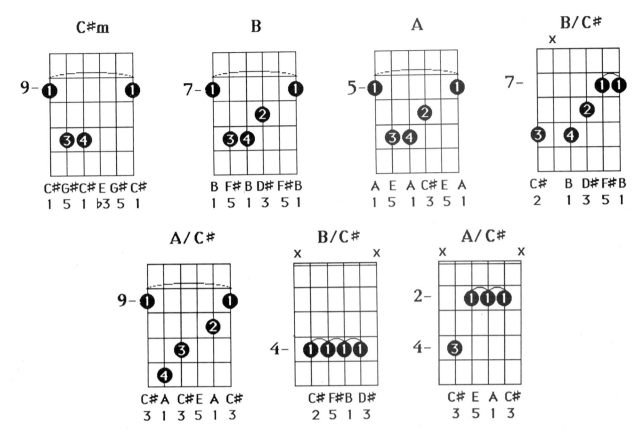

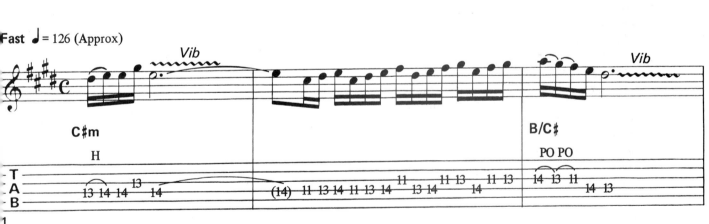

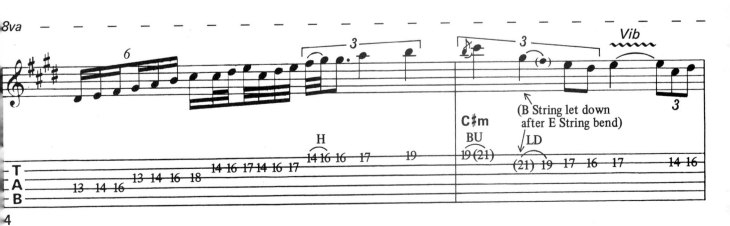

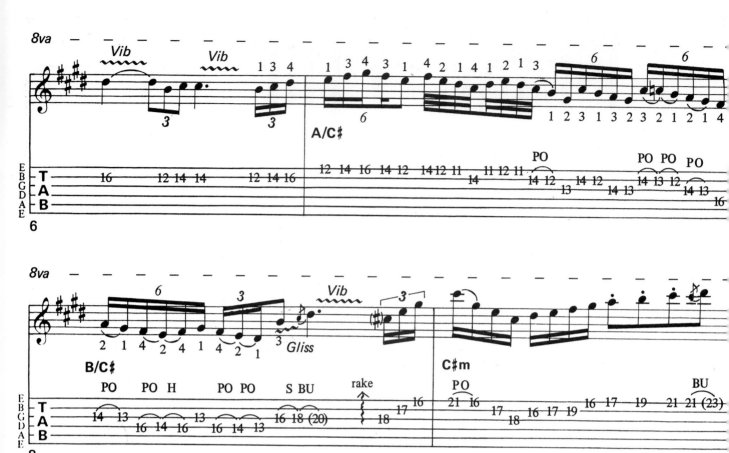

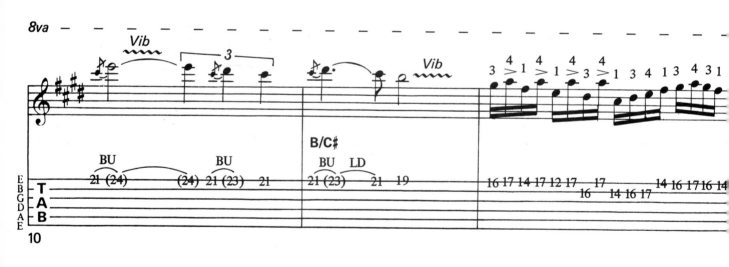

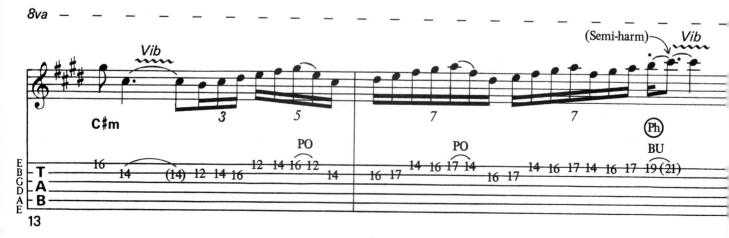

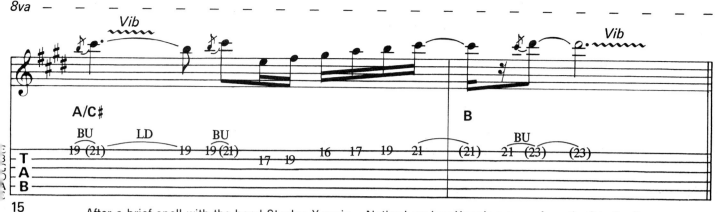

15

After a brief spell with the band Steeler, Yngwie Malmsteen joined forces with ex-Rainbow vocalist Graham Bonnet to form the band Alcatrazz. This solo is taken from their first album and is a fine example of the kind of virtuosic guitar playing which has made Yngwie one of the most influential rock guitarists of the 80s. It uses one scale type throughout, the C# aeolian mode/natural minor scale:

```
C#  D#  E   F#  G#  A   B   C#
1   2   b3  4   5   b6  b7  1
```

although a number of arpeggio and passing note ideas are also used.

The five note phrase at the start of bar 1 is written D#, E, E, G# and E, which is obviously what I believe was played. However, as the first couple of notes are a little unclear you may wish to play the live version of the phrase which is C#, D#, E, and E.

The 'answer' to the opening phrase runs from bars 2-3 and is comprised of some tasteful and melodic scale figures which, in common with all the scale based runs in this solo, should be played using strict alternate (up and down) picking. Bar 4 contains another fast ascending scale passage.

Notice here how Yngwie crosses from the G to the B string by playing the same note on both strings (C#s 2nd beat).

Bars 5 and 6 feature a fairly simple melodic pattern phrased in triplets, followed in bars 7-10 by some complex scale/arpeggio ideas. As the left hand fingerings for this section are quite awkward, I would suggest that you memorise them before attempting to build the passage up to speed. Also, the first 3 notes of the C# minor arpeggio in bar 8-9 should be played with a single downwards pick stroke (rake) and the 6th and 7th notes (E and C#) with an upwards pick stroke.

Bars 10-11 contain some string bending ideas, which will need to be pitched very carefully to sound effective.

The closing section in bars 12-16 begins with some characteristic pedal tone ideas (bar 12) and is followed by some combined scale and arpeggio figures. Notice in this how the arpeggios outline the chords of C#m and D major, and also how the phrasing during the first two beats of bar 14 is fairly unusual, falling in even groups of seven (septolets).

From the Alcatrazz album 'No Parole From Rock And Roll'. ©IMP.

87

# BRIAN MAY
# BOHEMIAN RHAPSODY

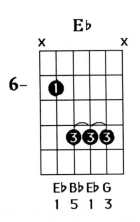

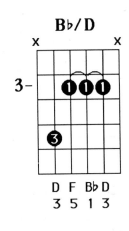

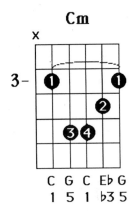

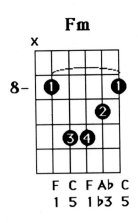

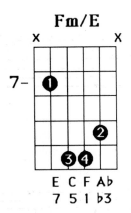

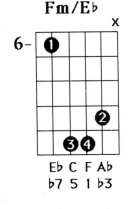

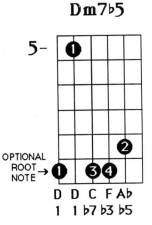

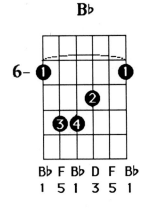

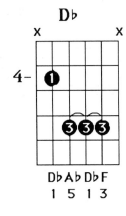

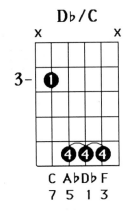

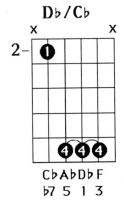

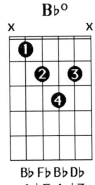

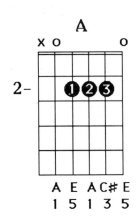

**Fairly Slow** ♩ = 70 (Approx)

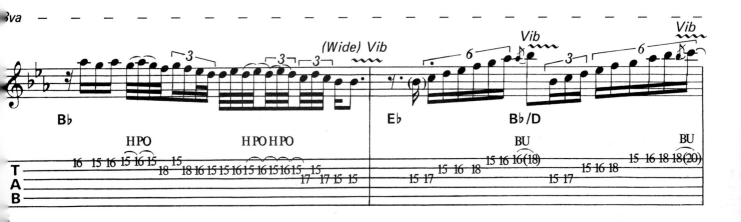

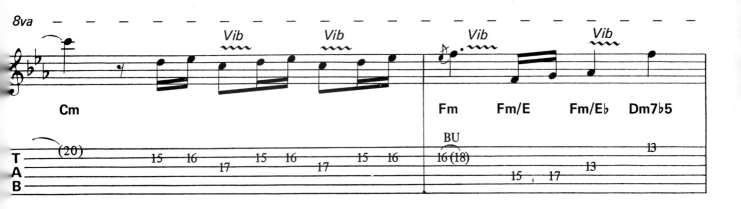

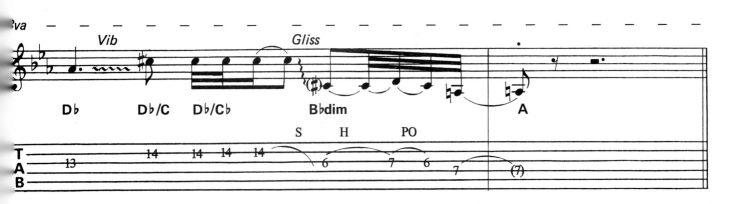

89

*Bohemian Rhapsody* was one of Queen's biggest ever selling singles and Brian May's solo on the track is undoubtedly one of the most memorable he's ever recorded. It centres around two scales, namely the C minor pentatonic:

```
C  Eb  F  G  Bb  C
1  b3  4  5  b7  1
```

and C natural minor/aeolian mode:

```
C  D  Eb  F  G  Ab  Bb  C
1  2  b3  4  5  b6  b7  1
```

The only notes outside these two scale forms are the C#s in the final two bars, which are played in anticipation of the modulation (key change) to A major.

Technically this solo's not unduly difficult and the only part likely to cause problems is the run in bar 5. On the third beat of this run Brian plays a trill between the D and Eb. The phrasing of this isn't quite as metrical as it appears on paper, so treat the phrasing as a guide.

The chord voicing suggestions represent a cross between the accompanying keyboard harmony and the descending guitar or bass line. Some of the voicings involve quite difficult stretches and will take some practice, however, if you persevere you should find that they will provide a satisfactory guitar accompaniment.

The solo was played on Brian's famous home made guitar, using an old English sixpence for a pick, through VOX amps.

# BRIAN MAY
# CRAZY LITTLE THING CALLED LOVE

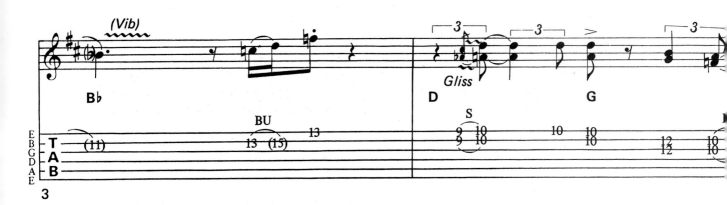

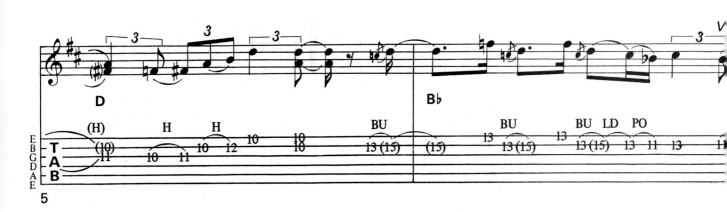

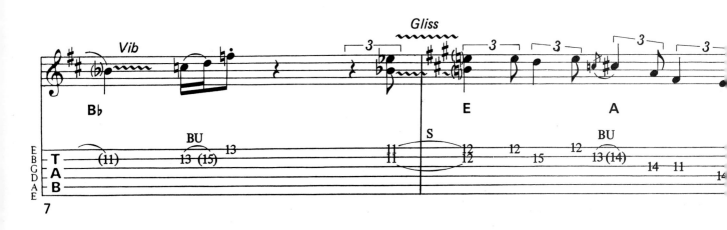

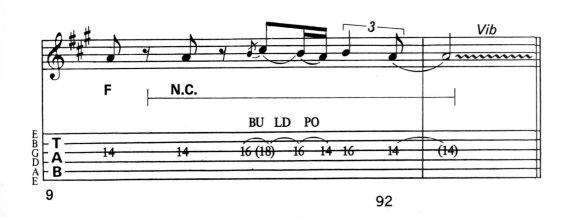

The fill preceding the solo uses the notes:

```
D   E   F    F#   G   A   Bb   B   C   D
1   2   b3   3    4   5   b6   6   b7  1
```

As both the F# and Bb are played as passing notes this could be seen as D dorian mode:

```
D   E   F    G   A   B   C    D
1   2   b3   4   5   6   b7   1
```

with the major 3rd (F#) and minor sixth (Bb) included for the purpose of adding some 'chromatic colour'. All other scales are mentioned below.

The unaccompanied opening bar consists of some repetitive two note chords (1 and 5 of D). The first of these is approached by a semi-tone slide (7-1 and b5-5) and is very reminiscent of the kind of device often found in Chuck Berry's solos.

In bars 2-3 Brian alters his note selection to correspond with the Bb chord change by playing a phrase derived from the Bb major pentatonic scale:

```
Bb   C   D   F   G   Bb
1    2   3   5   6   1
```

Notice also, the use of second (C)-major third (D) bends, and how one of these bends is followed by the fifth (F) played on the E string in bar 3. This type of lick is very much a characteristic of most country playing styles.

Bars 4-5 begin with more two note chord ideas (1 and 5, followed by 4 and 6) which lead into a couple of cliche b3-3 hammer ons and a short phrase that uses notes from the D major pentatonic scale:

```
D   E   F#   A   B   D
1   2   3    5   6   1
```

Bars 6-7 in common with bars 2-3 feature yet more Bb major pentatonic 'country' string bending ideas. As you play these, or indeed any of the string bends in this solo, make sure you remember not to apply any vibrato ('non vibrato' string bending is yet another trait of country/early rock 'n' roll styles).

The closing three bars feature a couple of phrases which have once again been structured in accordance with the underlying chord changes. Notice how in bar 7 the double stop (E and B) has been played at the 12th fret to correspond with the accompanying E chord, and how the C-C# bend against the A chord results in another rendition of the blusey cliche b3-3 effect mentioned earlier.

This solo was played on a Fender Telecaster which was most probably put through one or two (or more) Vox AC30s.

From the Queen album 'The Game' (EMI EMA795). Also available on 'Queen's Greatest Hits' (EMI EMTV30). 1979 Queen Music Ltd/EMI Music Publishing Ltd/International Music Publications.

# GARY MOORE
# EMPTY ROOMS

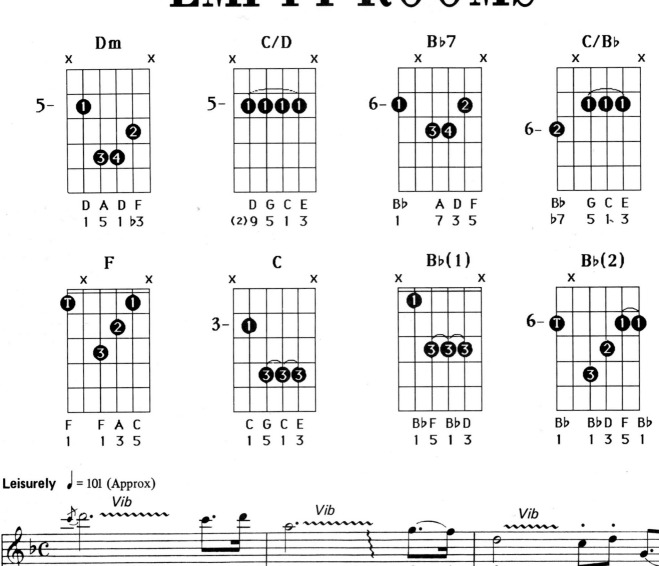

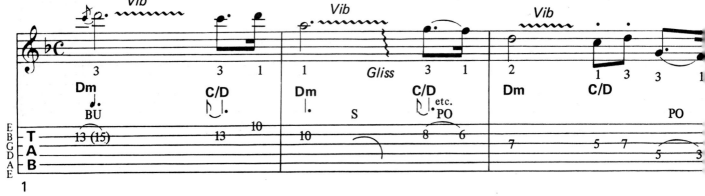

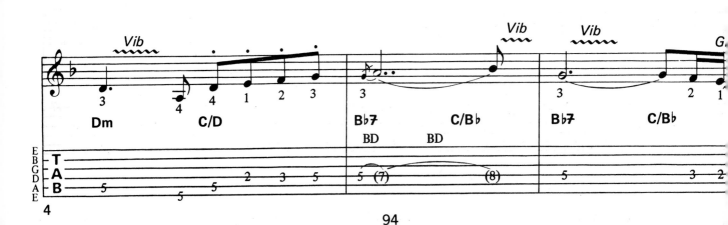

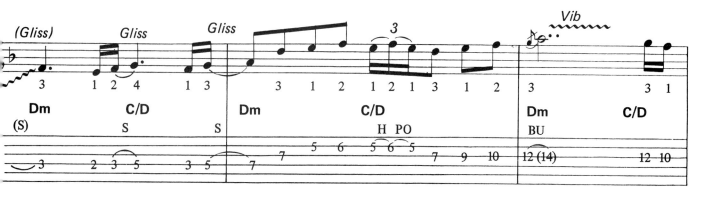

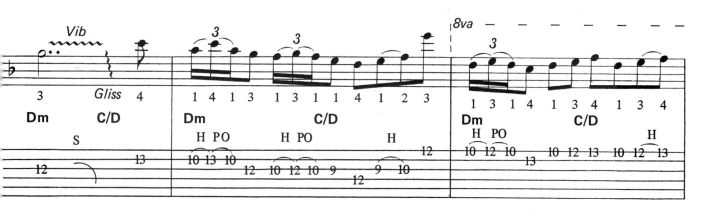

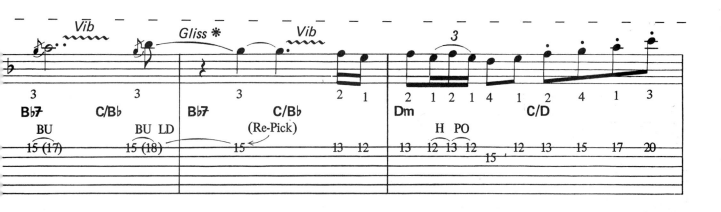

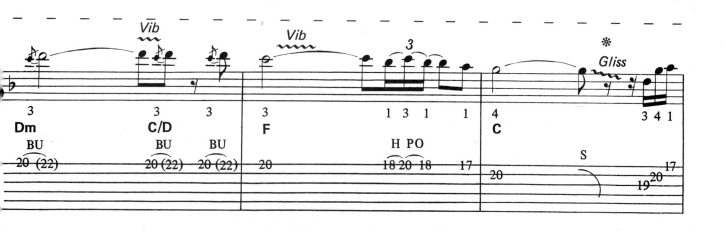

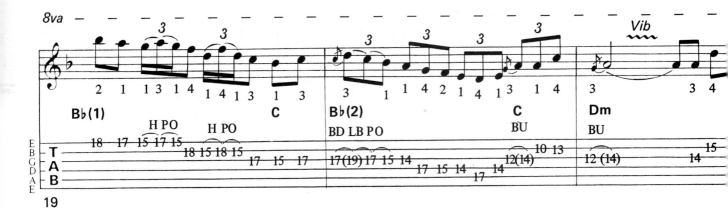

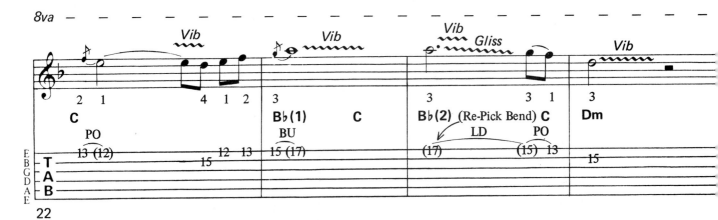

*Empty Rooms* is a fine example of the melodic side of Gary Moore's melodic/aggressive playing style. For this solo Gary uses the D minor pentatonic:

| D | F | G | A | Bb | C |
|---|---|---|---|----|---|
| 1 | b3 | 4 | 5 | b7 | 1 |

and the D aeolian mode/natural minor scale:

| D | E | F | G | A | Bb | C | D |
|---|---|---|---|---|----|---|---|
| 1 | 2 | b3 | 4 | 5 | b6 | b7 | 1 |

As you play, one of your main aims shoud be to try to recreate the 'feel' and metrical accuracy displayed on the recorded version. The rests shown on the music at points marked with an asterisk indicate that nothing new is played, but the let down bends can still be heard.

Make sure that you carefully follow all staccato markings – dots above the note heads – as they are vitally important to the effectiveness of the phrasing. The fingerings given for string bends indicate only the finger that rests on the first fret of the bend. You should try to assist the given finger with any other available fingers, however.

From the Gary Moore album 'Victims Of The Future' (Virgin Records D1X2). © 1981 Ten Music Ltd.

# GARY MOORE
# OUT IN THE FIELDS

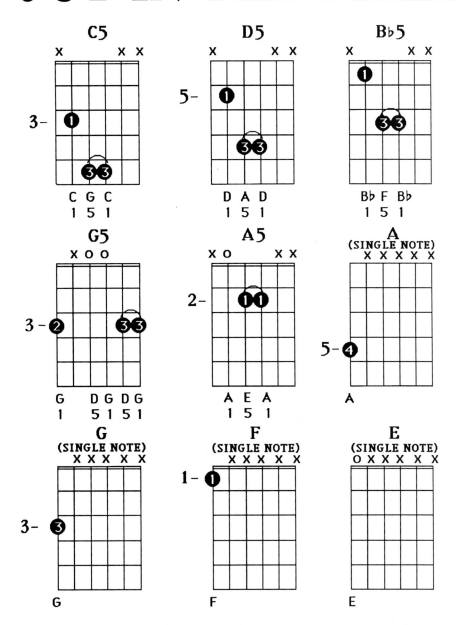

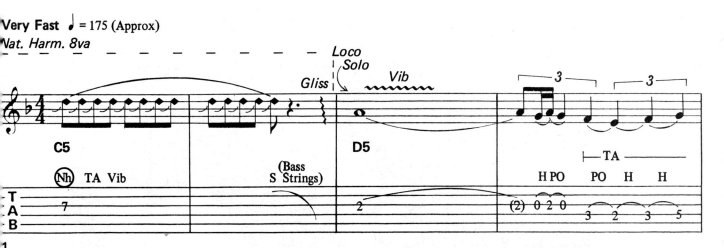

**Very Fast** ♩ = 175 (Approx)

Nat. Harm. 8va

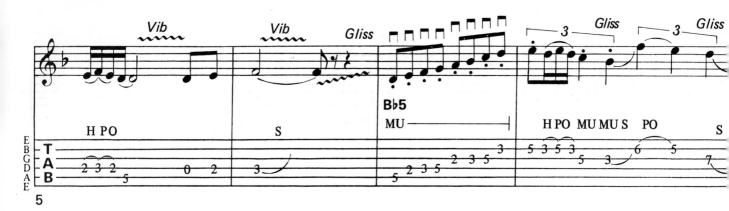

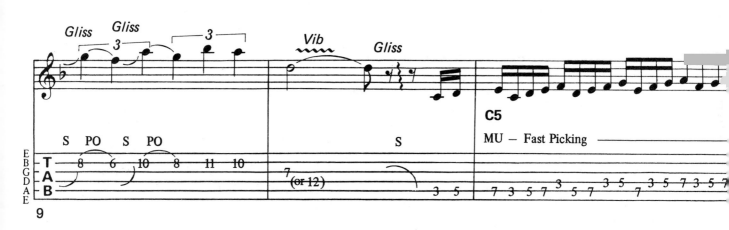

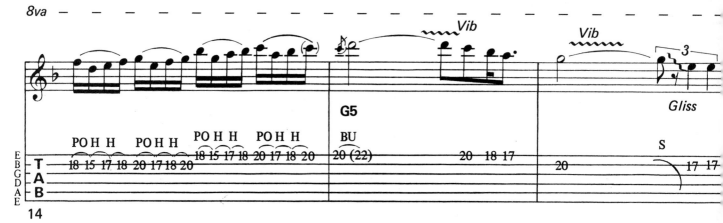

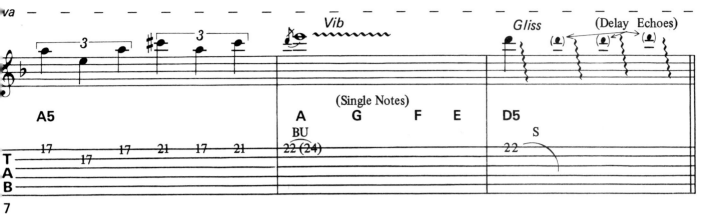

**A5**                                   (Single Notes)

*Vib*     *Gliss*     (Delay Echoes)

A      G     F     E      **D5**

BU                    S

17   17   21   17   21   22 (24)           22

17

7

This solo uses the D aeolian mode/natural minor scale:

| D | E | F | G | A | Bb | C | D |
|---|---|---|---|---|----|---|---|
| 1 | 2 | b3 | 4 | 5 | b6 | b7 | 1 |

The only occasion when Gary goes 'outside' this scale form is in bar 17 when he plays two C#s (C# is the major seventh of D/major third of A).

As far as playing is concerned it's best to pick the harmonic (D) in bars 1-2, then quickly depress and release the tremolo arm a number of times in order to produce the notated rhythm.

The last three notes of bar 4 (E, F and G) should be played by depressing and releasing the tremolo arm as you pull off from the F to the E, and again as you hammer on from the E to the F, and the F to the G.

In bar 7 every note of the scale is heavily muted via the right hand palm and picked using consecutive downstrokes.

The run in bars 11-14 is undoubtedly the most difficult part of the solo. To play it at the correct speed you will need a good left hand stretch and a very solid alternate picking and slurring technique. If you don't possess these attributes this run should make a challenging study in such techniques. Incidentally, the right hand motion needed to pick the first part of this run is closer to tremolo picking (up and downstrokes played as fast as possible) than to normal alternate picking.

Remember, the fingerings shown in the tab are editorial. If you find them awkward I would suggest you find others to suit your preference and use them instead.

# VINNIE MOORE
# LIFEFORCE

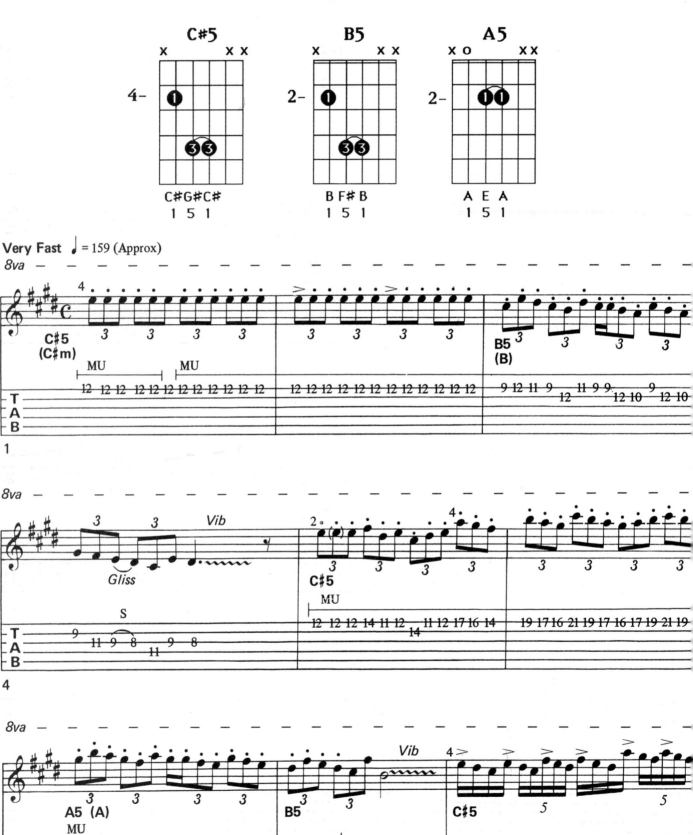

This transcription features the second solo from *Lifeforce*, a track on Vinnie Moore's recent album, 'Minds Eye'. Unlike the first solo, which is played in a more neo-classical vein, it contains many of the devices that are often found in Al Di Meola's playing style, especially the muted alternate picking, phrasing and melodic patterns. Indeed, Vinnie Moore has often cited Al Di Meola as being a main influence.

The solo is based around a single scale, the C# aeolian mode/natural minor scale:

C#  D#  E  F#  G#  A  B  C#
1   2   b3  4   5  b6  b7  1

Technically, it is a very challenging solo and you would probably be well advised to memorise it first, then to work at building each section up to speed gradually.

The muted passages in bars 1-3, 5-8 and 13 should all be played with the strings heavily damped by the right hand palm. If you don't normally use this kind of muted playing technique, you might find the restriction of movement – from resting your hand on the strings – will slow down your picking speed. It is worth persevering with this technique, however, as muted picking can produce some very useful and effective percussive ideas.

The section which runs from bar 9 through to bar 12 is obviously the most demanding part of the solo. Here Vinnie plays many of the phrases polyrhythmically across the beat, which results in the accents falling unpredictably in irregular places. The best way to approach this would probably be to learn the phrases in relation to the notated accents and then work at fitting the appropriate number of melodic/scale figures into each bar.

The term 'rake' in bars 13 and 14 indicates that the arpeggios should be played with glide strokes. The pick direction should correspond to the direction of the arrows which, in all cases, indicates downstrokes.

The bracketed chord designations represent the implied harmony and the accompanying chords are the unbracketed '5' power chords.

A final point, the solo was played on an Ibanez guitar through Peavey amps.

Taken from the Vinnie Moore album 'Minds Eye' (Roadrunner/Shrapnel Records RR9635).

102

# ALAN MURPHY
# DON'T LOOK DOWN

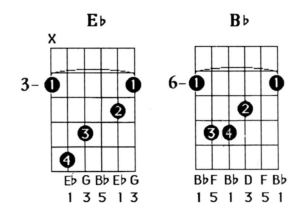

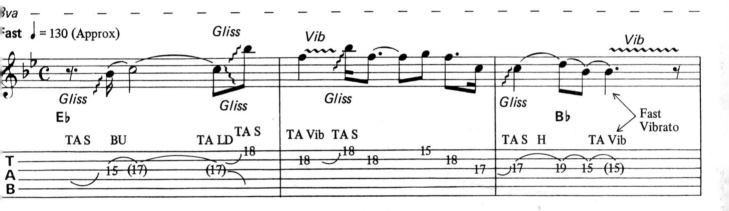

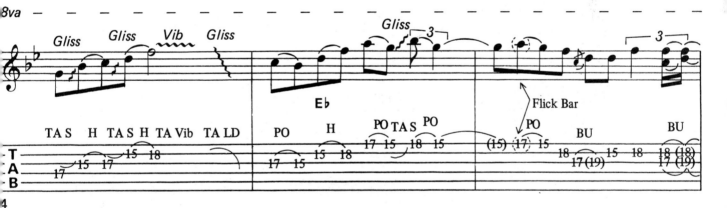

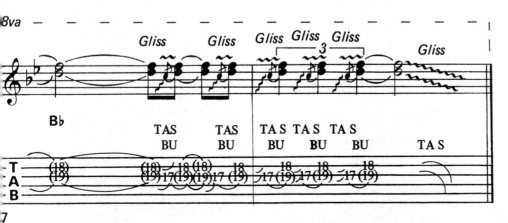

This solo is based around the Bb major pentatonic scale:

Bb  C  D  F  G  Bb
1   2  3  5  6  1

The only other note used in the solo is the A in bars 5 and 6, which is the #11 of the accompanying Eb chord.

One of the most prominent features of this solo is the widespread use of tremolo arm techniques, the most common of which is where you quickly depress and release the bar whilst picking a note. This results in an effect similar in sound to a conventional left hand slide and is indicated above the tab by the TA S designations.

As you play the A (first beat, bar 6) you should flick the bar with your right hand fourth finger, making the tremolo rock quickly backwards and forwards. Provided your tremolo arm is set up correctly, this should produce the gurgling sound that can be heard on the record.

In bars 1, 2 and 3 the vibrato is achieved by the tremolo arm rather than the normal left hand technique. As you do this, make sure you keep it as even as possible and that you listen to the record to get an idea of the correct speed and width.

From the Go West album 'Go West' (CBS CHR1495). ©CBS

# ALAN MURPHY
# SOS

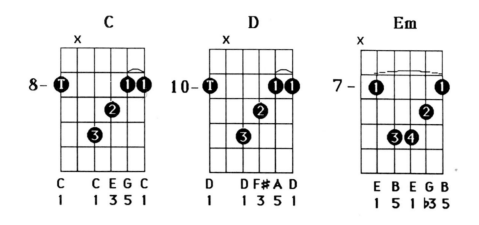

Fast ♩ = 128 (Approx)

8va throughout — — — —

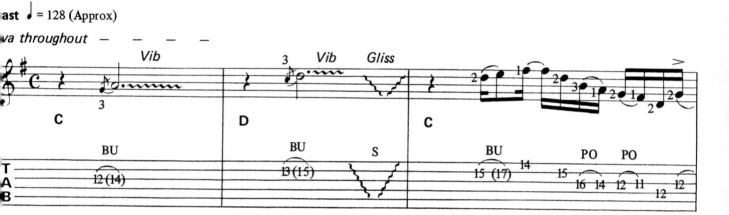

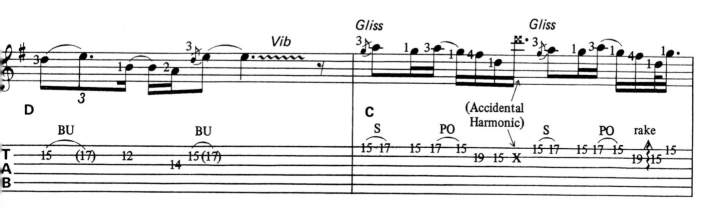

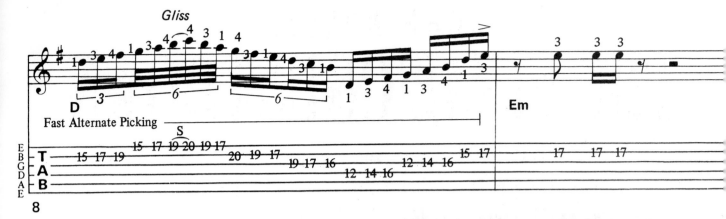

**8**

Alan uses one scale here, the E aeolian mode/ natural minor scale:

| E | F# | G | A | B | C | D | E |
|---|----|---|---|---|---|---|---|
| 1 | 2 | b3 | 4 | 5 | b6 | b7 | 1 |

The first point of interest here is that in bar 4 the tremolo arm should be depressed and released at the same time as you hammer on from the G to A, and again as you slide up to the F#, while the phrase which runs from the last semi-quaver of bar 4 (G) to the end of bar 6 (E), should be lightly picked (alternate picking) and phrased in a 'swinging' jazz style. If you listen to the record you'll hear what I mean.

Bar 8 is perhaps the most demanding section of the solo. It should once again be played using fast alternate picking, although if this causes problems, you may find it easier to use slurs initially (hammer ons/pull offs), and introduce the alternate picking as and when you feel comfortable.

In transcribing this solo I wasn't sure whether or not Alan actually played the run at the end of bar 8 which starts on the D, first semi-quaver, third beat, through to the end. However, as he definitely plays it live, I have given a suggested fingering.

# THE FINAL COUNTDOWN

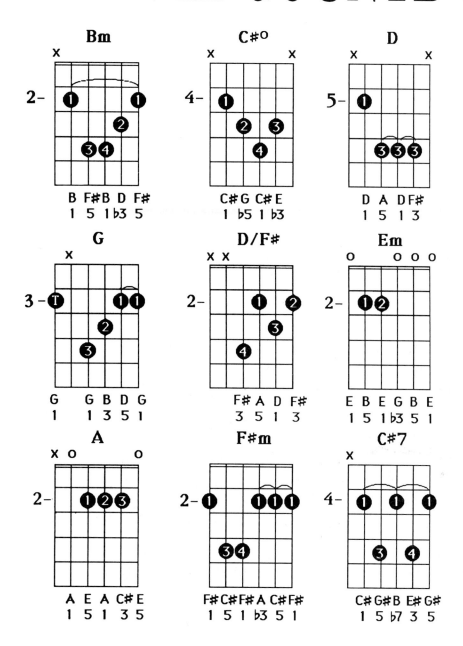

**Moderately Fast** ♩ = 118 (Approx)

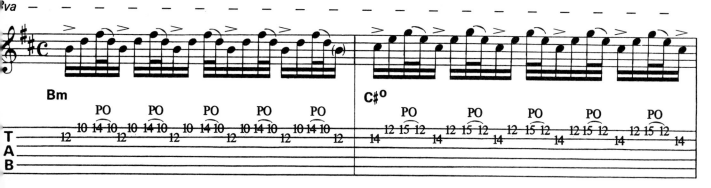

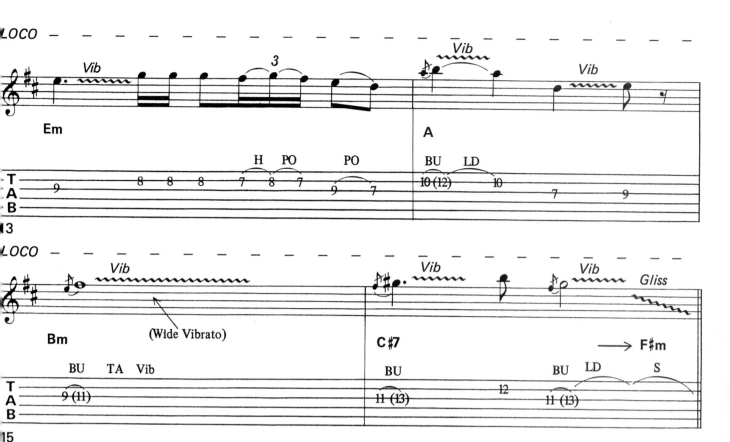

Although most associated with Kee Marcello the original, and recorded, solo on *The Final Countdown* was played by John Norum, who left Europe shortly after their first album was released. John uses the B aeolian mode/natural minor scale:

B   C#  D   E   F#  G   A   B
1   2   b3  4   5   b6  b7  1

and the B blues scale;

B   D   E   F   F#  A   B
1   b3  4   b5  5   b7  1

The main focus point of this solo is certainly the fast arpeggio figures played during bars 1-4 and again in bars 9-12. These all correspond to the chords in the accompanying progression – Bm, C#dim, D and G – and are very reminiscent of the kind of pseudo-classical ideas often heard in Ritchie Blackmore's playing.

Rhythmically these arpeggios are quite complex and may prove difficult to perform in time, due to the thirty-second note slurs between the third and fourth notes of each repetitive four note figure. This

effectively gives each pattern a total duration of only three sixteenths, and subsequently results in the displacement of each accented first note. It also means the accents fall polyrhythmically on semiquavers 1, 4, 7, 10 and 13.

To hear precisely what I mean and to practise this section initially, you may find it helpful to work with a slowed down version of the track. Play the single at 33rpm and re-finger the passage in F#m.

The remainder of the solo is very straightforward, the only phrase likely to cause problems comes in bars 7-8. This uses the B blues scale to produce a very interesting, catchy phrase which will probably end up sounding more fluid if it is memorised first. Practise it slowly and methodically, carefully building up to tempo over a period of time. Also, notice how the major 6th (G#, third beat bar 7) and b5 (F) help to make this phrase sound a little more colourful than many of the similar minor pentatonic based phrases of the genre.

From Europe's single *The Final Countdown* (Epic/CBS A7127). ©1986/87 Doors Music, EMI Music Publishing (Sweden). Sub-Published by EMI Music Publishing Ltd, London, WC2H 0LD

# JIMMY PAGE
# STAIRWAY TO HEAVEN

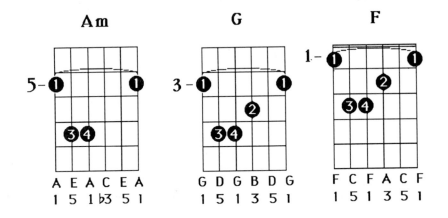

INTRO

**Slow** ♩ = 72 (Approx)

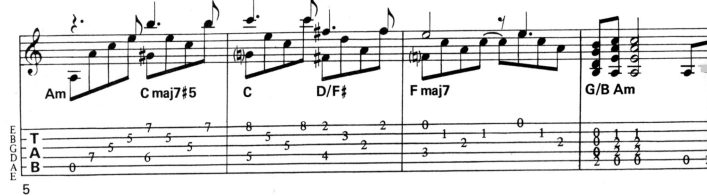

3

**SOLO**

Moderate ♩ = 97 (Approx)

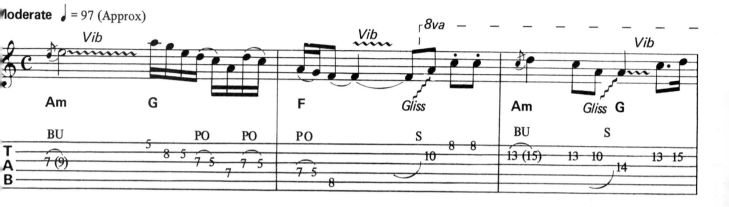

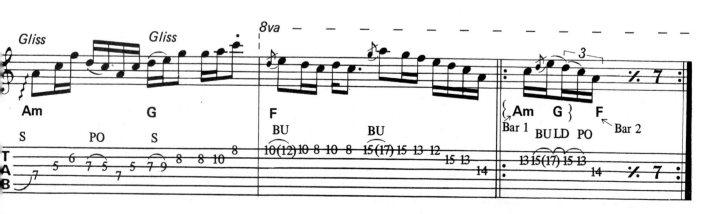

111

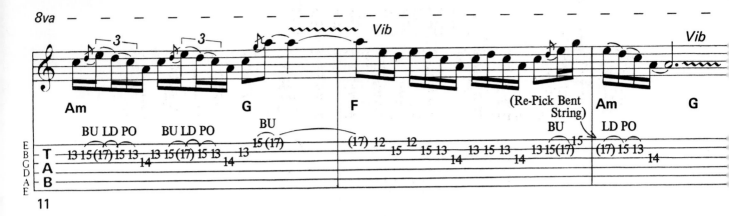

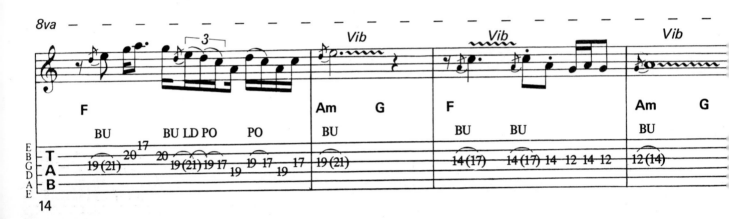

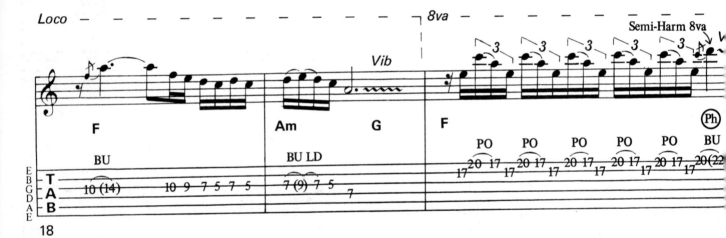

I have transcribed both the solo and the introduction from *Stairway To Heaven* here, the latter being without doubt one of the most popular and memorable guitar parts ever recorded. Throughout the solo the A minor pentatonic scale is used almost exclusively:

| A | C | D | E | G | A |
|---|---|---|---|---|---|
| 1 | b3 | 4 | 5 | b7 | 1 |

the only exception to this being when the note F (b6) is played as either part of the melodic line or accented over the F chord (bars 2, 6, 7, 8 and 18). The inclusion of this F results in an overall note content of:

| A | C | D | E | F | G |
|---|---|---|---|---|---|
| 1 | b3 | 4 | 5 | b6 | b7 |

Notice how the accompanying chords can all be derived from these notes.

On the record the introduction sounds as though it was played on a steel string acoustic, but it can be played on more or less any guitar, in fact, when Jimmy plays it live he usually uses the six string neck of his 6/12 string Gibson SG.

Technically it is easiest to play when fingerpicked, but it can also be played by using the pick and fingers together. To hear the recorded guitar part more clearly, try adjusting the balance control so you can only hear the left stereo channel, as the guitar is mixed to that side.

The solo is again fairly straightforward technically speaking, although you may need to be careful with the A to C (tone and a half) bend in bar 16 and the F to A (two tone) bend in bar 18. Notice also the open G (first eighth note, bar 6). I'm not sure if this was played intentionally or by accident, but it sounds fine and you might find that it's more comfortable to play it on the fifth fret of the D string.

Taken from Led Zeppelin's fourth album 'Led Zeppelin' (Atlantic K5008). © WEA.

# JIMMY PAGE
# WHOLE LOTTA LOVE

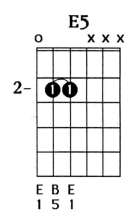

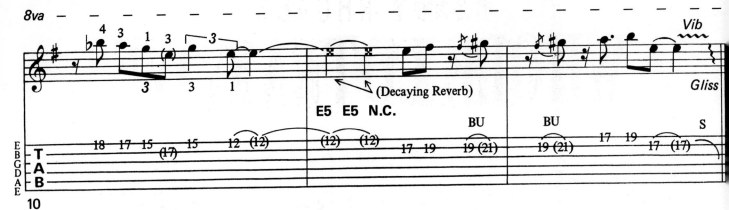

Jimmy Page's solo on *Whole Lotta Love* is an excellent example of his mastery of blues/rock phrasing, dynamics and 'feel'. In terms of scales it uses all three common blues forms, the E blues scale:

| E | G | A | Bb | B | D | E |
|---|---|---|----|---|---|---|
| 1 | b3 | 4 | b5 | 5 | b7 | 1 |

the E minor pentatonic:

| E | G | A | B | D | E |
|---|---|---|---|---|---|
| 1 | b3 | 4 | 5 | b7 | 1 |

and the E major pentatonic:

| E | F# | G# | B | C# | E |
|---|----|----|---|----|---|
| 1 | 2 | 3 | 5 | 6 | 1 |

The solo is made up of six phrases which, for our purposes, can all be analysed separately.

The opening phrase runs from beat 4, bar 1 to the first down beat of bar 3 and is a simple blues phrase, using notes from the E blues scale position at the 12th fret.

The next phrase begins on the third up-beat of bar 3 and ends on the first eighth note of bar 5. This provides a nice contrast to the first idea by using the E minor pentatonic scale in combination with pull offs played low down the neck, ending on a low open E.

The third phrase in bars 5 and 6 is a common cliched, minor pentatonic idea.

The fourth phrase, from bars 7-9, feature a rather severe string bend which ascends by just over a major third from G nearly up to C. Notice that the notes which follow are from a mixture of both the minor and major pentatonic scales.

The fifth phrase in bars 9-11 begins with a bend from the fifth (B) up to the major sixth (C#) and is followed by another blues scale based idea.

The final phrase in bar 11-12 is a cliched, major pentatonic lick, in which the bend ascends from a second to a major third. Similar examples of this kind of idea can be found in Peter Green's solos on *Need Your Love So Bad*.

# RANDY RHOADS
# CRAZY TRAIN

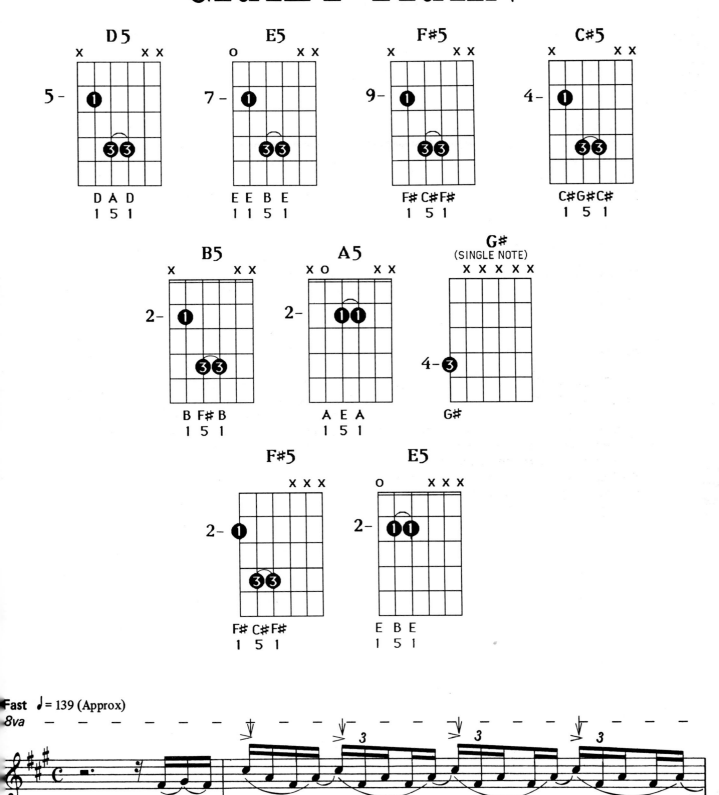

115

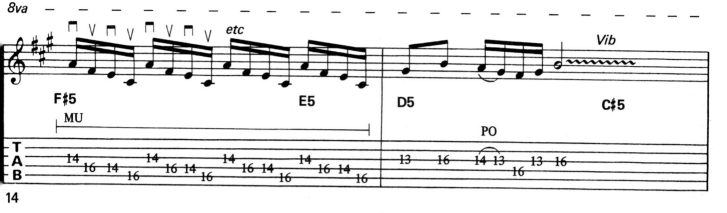

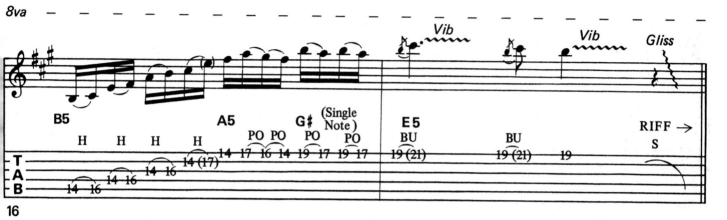

Randy Rhoads was a member of Ozzy Osbourne's band, Blizzard Of Oz, from 1979 until he died in March 1982. In mid 1987 a double live album in honour of this outstanding guitarist, aptly entitled 'Tribute', was released and this version of his extremely popular solo on *Crazy Train* is taken from side one of that album.

The solo is based on the F# minor pentatonic scale:

| F# | A | B | C# | E | F# |
|----|-----|---|----|----|----|
| 1 | b3 | 4 | 5 | b7 | 1 |

the F# blues scale:

| F# | A | B | C | C# | E | F# |
|----|-----|---|----|----|----|----|
| 1 | b3 | 4 | b5 | 5 | b7 | 1 |

and the F# aeolian mode/natural minor scale:

| F# | G# | A | B | C# | D | E | F# |
|----|-----|-----|---|----|----|----|----|
| 1 | 2 | b3 | 4 | 5 | b6 | b7 | 1 |

The first three bars feature arpeggio figures which are played using two hand tapping. These figures outline the accompanying chords of F# minor and D major. On this live version Randy seems to finish playing the final D major arpeggio a little prematurely – on the first sixteenth/fourth beat – and as this makes the phrase shorter than that in the original solo, I have taken the liberty of adding the three notes required to conclude the phrase at the end of the bar.

In bar 4 Randy plays trills which alternate between the root and sixth of the accompanying B

and A chords. These are connected by a very fast left hand position shift which, if executed correctly, leaves the trill sounding as if it is let down by the tremolo arm.

Bars 5-7 contain some very straightforward ideas. One point worth mentioning, however, is that the descending line of A, G# and F# in bar 6 is repeated in reverse order in bar 7. This type of idea is often seen in guitar solos and is effective because the second phrase acts as a kind of imitative musical answer to the first.

The phrase in bars 8-9 uses the F# blues and pentatonic scales in combination with fast slurring. As you play through this, try to keep the phrasing as metrical as it is on the record. Incidentally, the D on the third sixteenth note/second beat is not found in either of the aforementioned scale types. It can, however, be regarded as either a passing note, or as the b6 derived from the natural minor scale.

Bars 10-12 feature an ascending series of slurred trills, which were one of Randy's most recognisable traits. A good deal of practice will probably be needed before they can be played with the type of precision displayed on the record!

The remainder of the solo is comprised entirely of pentatonic based phrases. The repetitive figures in bar 14 should be played using alternate picking. However, if you find this difficult it might help to use a pull off between the second and third sixteenth notes of each figure (F# to E).

117

# RANDY RHOADS
# REVELATION
# (MOTHER EARTH)

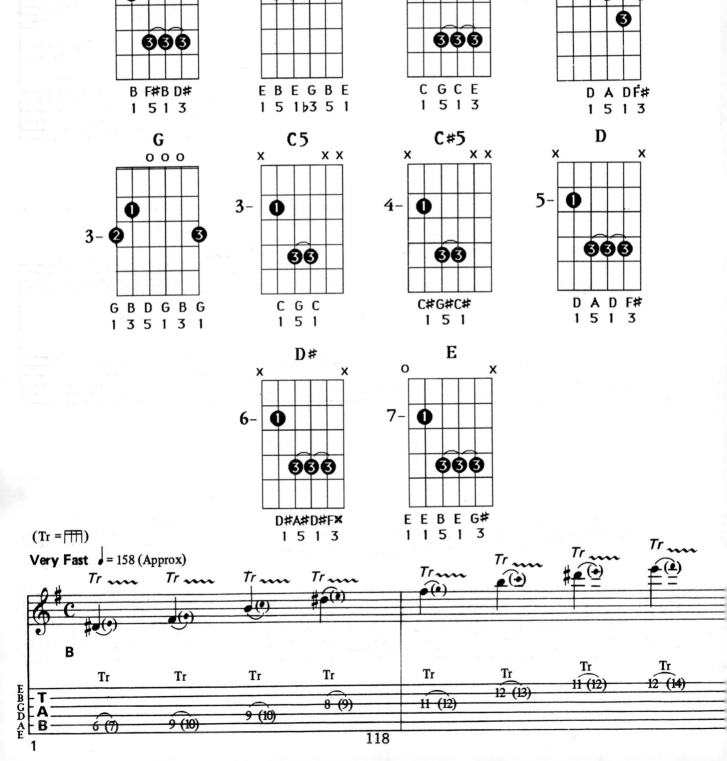

119

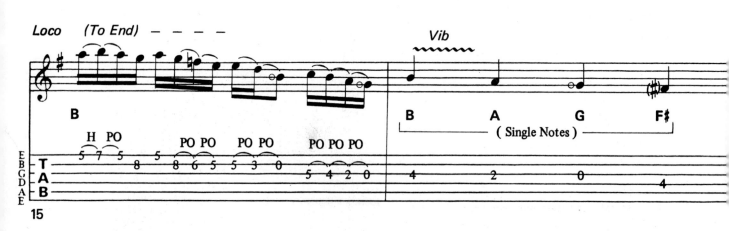

**Progression** — **Em D G B / X 3 C5 C#5 D D# E ‖**

Randy Rhoads' solo on *Revelation (Mother Earth)* is, to my mind, one of the most impressive solos he ever recorded. It's based on two scale types, namely the E aeolian mode/natural minor scale:

```
E  F#  G   A   B   C   D   E
1  2   b3  4   5   b6  b7  1
```

and the E phrygian mode;

```
E  F   G   A   B   C   D   E
1  b2  b3  4   5   b6  b7  1
```

Technically, this solo is very demanding and will probably require a good deal of practice to master. However, as it was most likely constructed, as opposed to improvised, the majority of phrases can be memorised fairly easily and if approached slowly, one section at a time, shouldn't be too difficult to come to terms with.

The first three bars feature slurred trills. In bars 1-2 the notes B, D# and F# outline the accompanying B major chord. In bar 3 Randy uses trills to ascend step-wise up to the high B. To perform these trills correctly you should pick the lower note, hammer on to the upper note, pull off to the lower note and then hammer on to the higher note. This cycle of hammer ons/pull offs should be completed once every quarter note beat, and should yield a clearly articulated sixteenth note pattern.

In bar 4 Randy plays a descending figure on the top E string which pivots on the pedal note of B (19th fret). This device is often found in classical music and is possibly a reference to Randy's earlier classical training: he was an accomplished classical guitarist, who at one time nearly gave up playing rock music in order to pursue a full time classical career.

The phrase in bars 5-6 begins with an E minor arpeggio that leads into some very melodic scale figures. These are contrasted in bars 7-8 by a phrase which is comprised of the rather unmelodious intervals of a flattened fifth (D#-A), a sharpened fourth (A-D#) and a major seventh (D#-D natural).

Bars 9-15 are where Randy's masterful slurring technique really comes to the fore. Notice how many of the phrases imitate each other and how the pedal point idea, discussed earlier, is used yet again in bar 14, only this time with the open E string as a lower pedal.

Bars 16-20 contain the riff patterns that precede the entry of the ascending theme, played to lead out of the song. As this theme is very simple it hasn't been notated, although the accompanying chord progression is shown below.

Incidentally, the solo was most probably played on one of Randy's Gibson Les Paul custom guitars, through Marshall amps.

From the Ozzy Osbourne album 'Tribute' (EPIC/CBS450475 1).

121

# RANDY RHOADS
# STEAL AWAY (THE NIGHT)

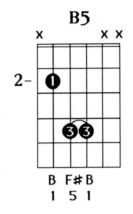

**Gm**

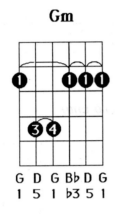

G D G Bb D G
1 5 1 b3 5 1

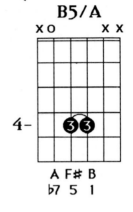

**B5**

B F# B
1 5 1

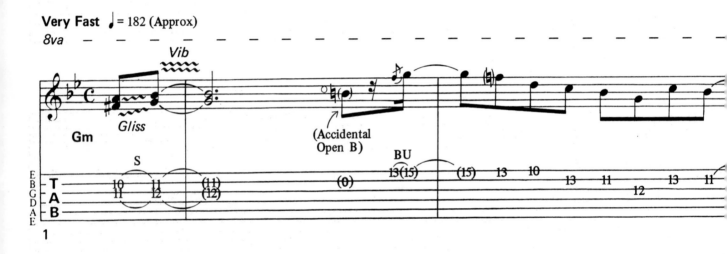

**B5/A**

A F# B
b7 5 1

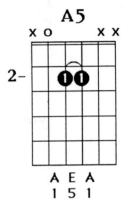

**A5**

A E A
1 5 1

**Very Fast** ♩ = 182 (Approx)

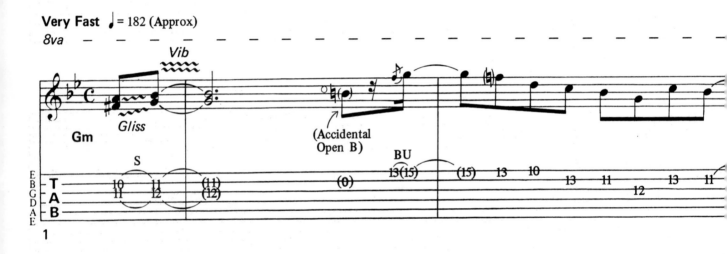

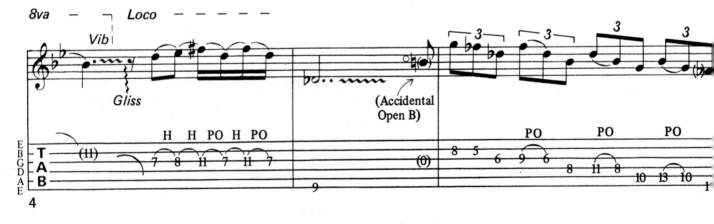

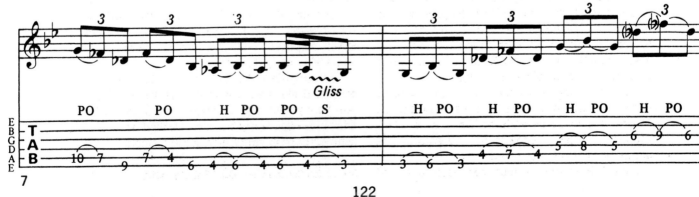

122

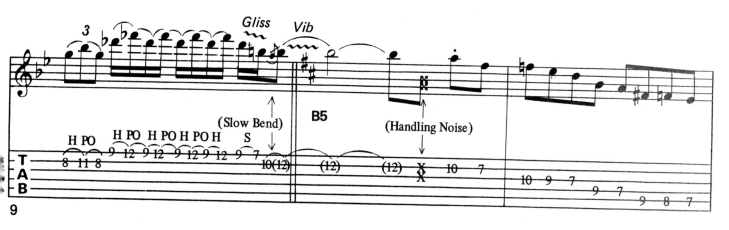

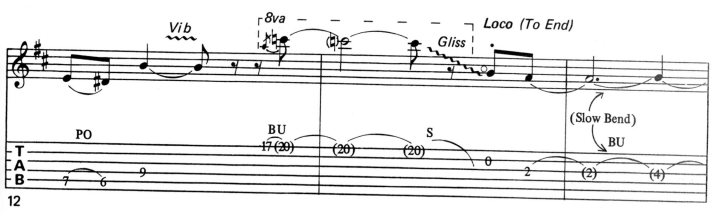

The two scales used here are the G minor pentatonic:

| G | Bb | C | D | F | G |
|---|----|---|---|---|---|
| 1 | b3 | 4 | 5 | b7 | 1 |

and the B blues scale:

| B | D | E | F | F# | A | B |
|---|---|---|---|----|---|---|
| 1 | b3 | 4 | b5 | 5 | b7 | 1 |

At the beginning of the solo the tune modulates to G minor, which Randy outlines by playing a two note chord of G and Bb (1 and b3 of G minor, bar 1). Notice how this diad is approached by a slide from a semitone below and how Randy adds vibrato in order to help it sustain a little longer.

Bars 2-5 contain a couple of simple phrases which use notes from the G minor pentatonic scale. The second of these ends on Db – a b5 which sounds rather unpleasant against the accompanying G minor chord.

Bars 6-9 feature a four bar ascending and descending phrase which uses notes from the arpeggio of G diminished seventh (G Bb Db Fb). This phrase is very difficult to get up to speed and unless you are used to diminished arpeggio playing it will probably take a lot of slow methodical practice.

In bars 10-12 Randy plays a simple run complying with the new key (B minor) and using notes from the B blues scale. At the end of this run is a major third D#. This results in a 'sweeter' ending than if Randy had used the D natural from the scale.

The minor third bend from A-C in bars 12-13, in common with the b5 and diminished arpeggio ideas mentioned earlier, is another dissonant or 'outside' note, in this case a b9.

Following the b7-key note bend in bars 14-15 is another B blues scale phrase (bars 16-17). Notice how Randy returns to the rhythm part at the end of this phrase by playing the notes on the A string in a semi-chromatic, rather than scalic fashion.

From the Ozzy Osbourne album 'Tribute' (EPIC/CBS 450475)

123

# RICHIE SAMBORA
# LIVIN' ON A PRAYER

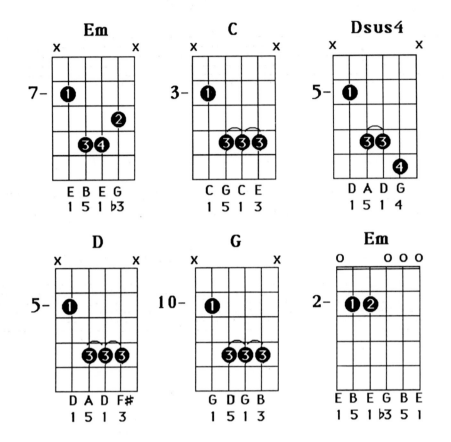

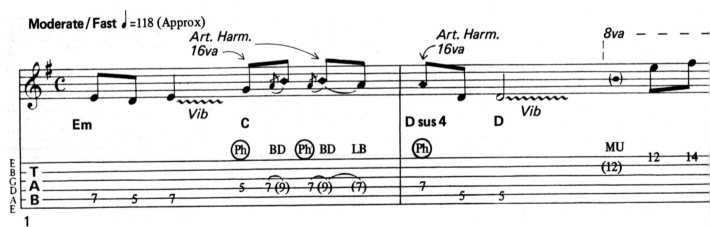

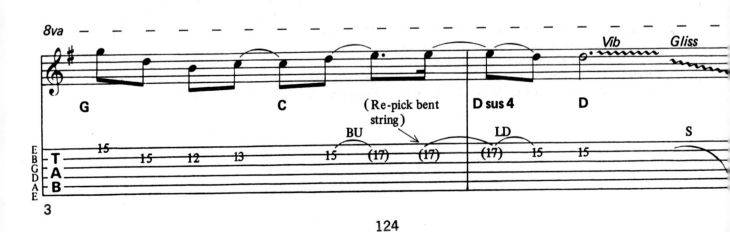

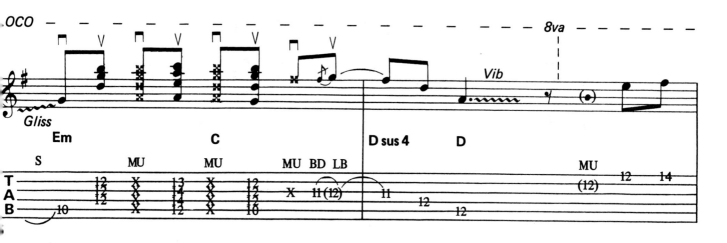

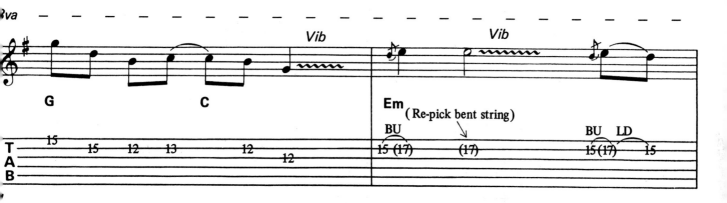

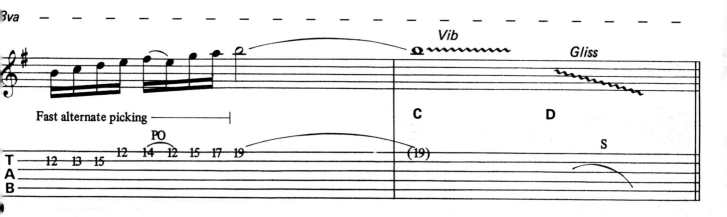

Here we have a solo which uses the E aeolian mode/natural minor scale exclusively:

| E | F# | G | A | B | C | D | E |
|---|----|----|---|---|---|---|---|
| 1 | 2 | b3 | 4 | 5 | b6 | b7 | 1 |

The pinched harmonics (Ph) in the first two bars should be produced by catching the string with the flesh of your right hand thumb immediately after striking the string with the pick.

Although the muted chords shown in bar 5 are barely audible, it is important that they are performed, otherwise the correct 'feel' of the syncopated chords will not come over very effectively. Likewise, the Bs sound as ghost, or slightly heard, notes in bars 2 and 6, and should be produced by playing a quick, downwards glide stroke across the 12th fret of the B and E strings.

From the Bon Jovi single *Livin' On A Prayer* (Vertigo/Polygram VER28). ©1986 Polygram Music Publishing Inc/Bon Jovi Publishing April Music Inc.

# CARLOS SANTANA
# BLACK MAGIC WOMAN

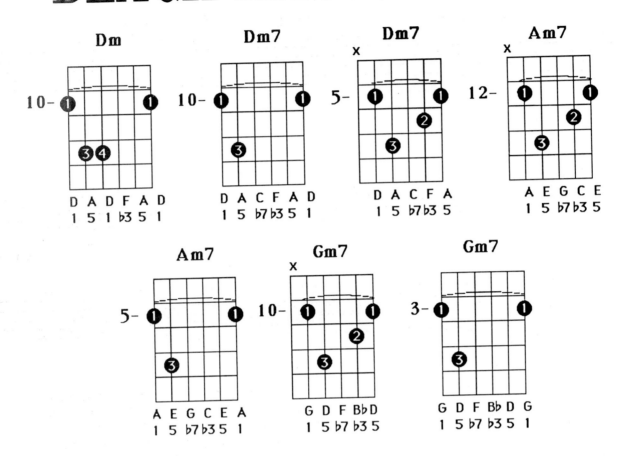

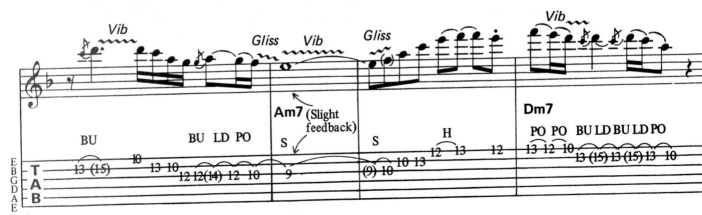

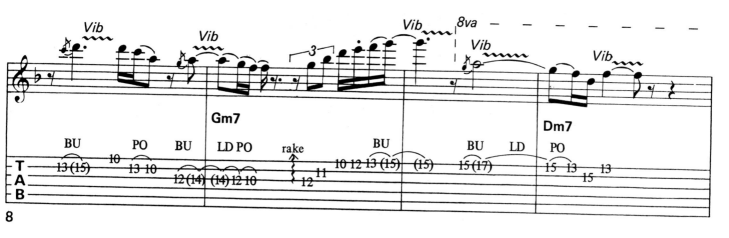

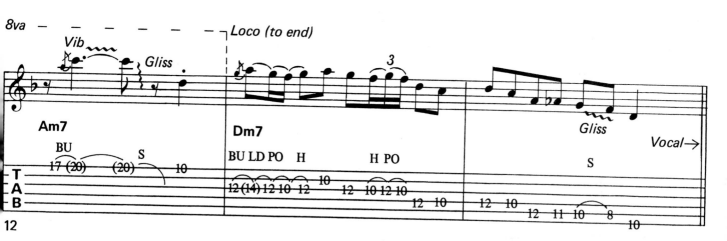

Carlos Santana's solo on Santana's version of Peter Green's *Black Magic Woman* is certainly one of the best known and most popular examples of his playing. The solo transcribed here is the one Carlos plays during the introduction to the track. It uses a combination of two scale types, the D minor pentatonic:

```
D   F   G   A   C   D
1   b3  4   5   b7  1
```

and the D aeolian mode/natural minor scale:

```
D   E   F   G   A   Bb  C   D
1   2   b3  4   5   b6  b7  1
```

Carlos leads into the solo by playing a two octave, D minor arpeggio. This is followed in bars 2-3 by the instantly recognisable opening phrase, which is a very simple, yet effective minor pentatonic based idea.

Bars 4-8 contain a number of question/answer phrases which use the minor pentatonic scale with the addition of a second (E). Notice how this note is played to correspond with the Am7 chord change in bars 5 and 6, and how it functions as a ninth against the Dm7 chord in bar 7. Another point of interest is the length of time that Carlos sustains the E in bars 5-6 – long sustain, often assisted by feedback, is one of Carlos Santana's most recognisable traits.

Carlos also plays notes to outline a chord change in bar 9, where Bb is played in correspondence with the change to Gm7 – Bb is the b3 of Gm7. Bars 10-15 use much the same ideas as those already mentioned, and the only things to watch out for are that the string bending is accurate (particularly on the minor third bend in 12, A-C) and that, in common with the rest of the solo, the vibrato is made to 'sing' in the manner exhibited on the record.

From the Santana compilation album 'The Very Best Of Santana' (TSA/228). © 1986 CBS/Arcade. (Originally recorded on the album 'Abraxis').

# MICHAEL SCHENKER
# INTO THE ARENA

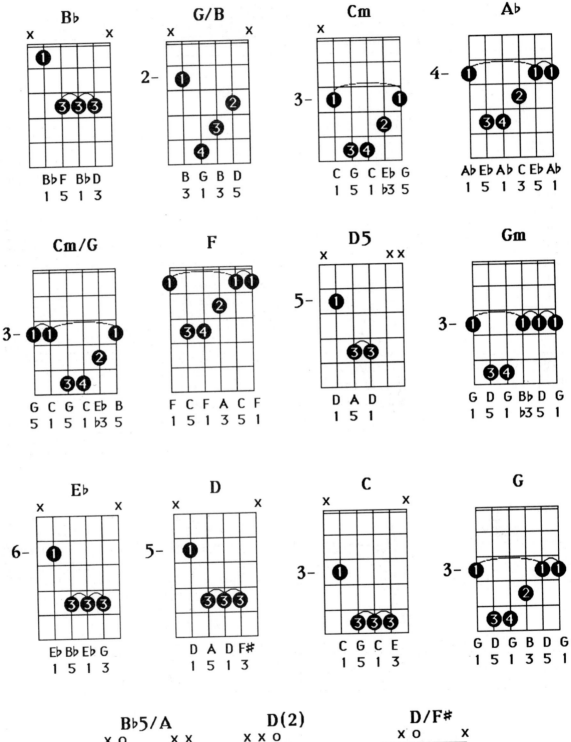

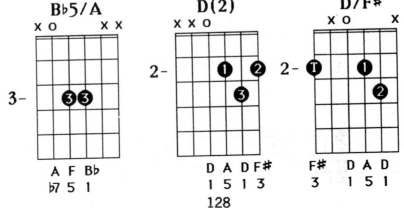

130

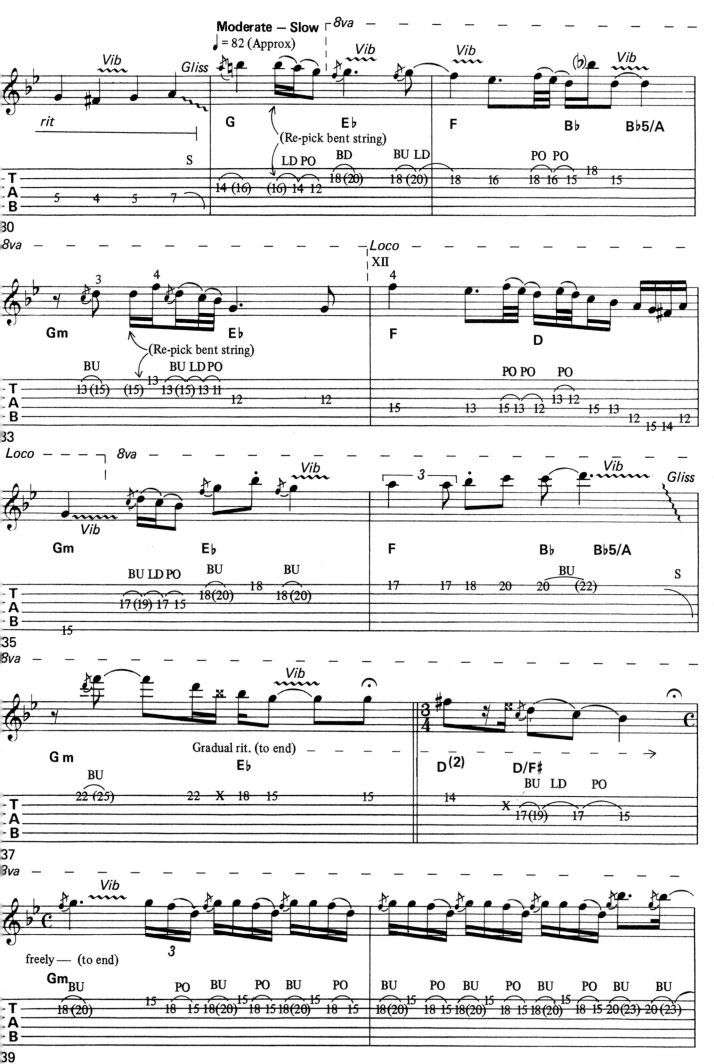

131

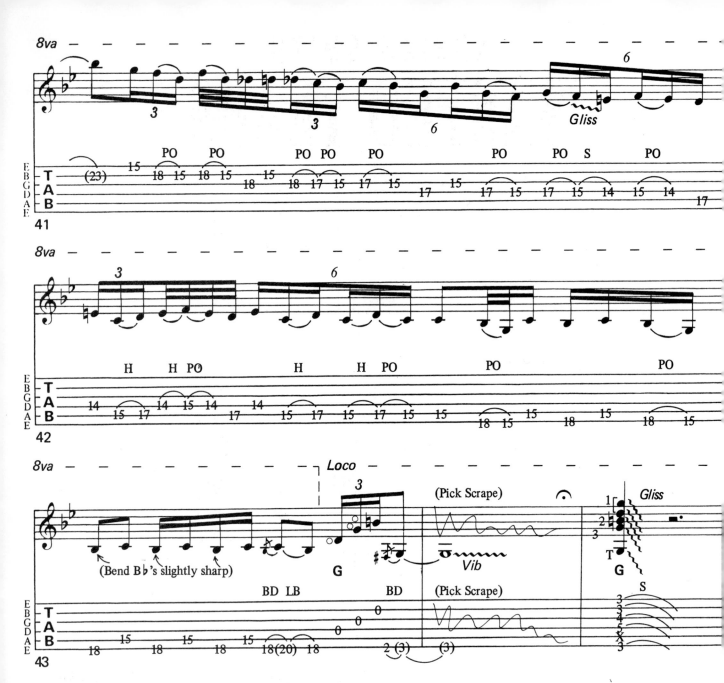

Into The Arena is one of Michael Schenker's most celebrated and widely acclaimed instrumental compositions and the solo, taken from the end of the track, is a good example of his lyrical and melodic guitar style. It relies heavily on three scale types, the G aeolian mode/natural minor scale:

```
G   A   Bb   C   D   Eb   F   G
1   2   b3   4   5   b6   b7  1
```

the G minor pentatonic scale:

```
G   Bb   C   D   F   G
1   b3   4   5   b7  1
```

and the G blues scale (closing section only):

```
G   Bb   C   Db   D   F   G
1   b3   4   b5   5   b7  1
```

The first 9 bars feature the arpeggio section which precedes the solo. On the original version of the track this was only played on keyboards, but as Michael definitely plays this section live I have given a suggested fingering.

Bars 20-21 feature an ascending/descending phrase, based around notes from the arpeggio of D7 (D F# A C). The fingering for this involves a number of quick position shifts which will probably require a fair amount of practice.

Throughout the solo a lot of the ideas make good use of chord tones. To study these further I would strongly recommend that you compare the notes on the solo to those contained in the accompaniment chord progression.

Technically the closing phrases in bars 39-43 are the most demanding part of the solo. Both slurring and bending ideas are used here to produce a series of fast repetitive riffs and descending figures. To perform this section correctly I would suggest that you work on it slowly at first, one bar at a time if necessary, only building up the tempo as it becomes more comfortable.

Incidentally, the solo was played on a customised Gibson Flying V through 50 watt Marshall amps with a Cry Baby Wah Wah for tone.

From the Michael Schenker Group album 'MSG' (CHR 1336). ©Shenker/ Chrysallis Music Ltd.

132

# ADRIAN SMITH
# WASTED YEARS

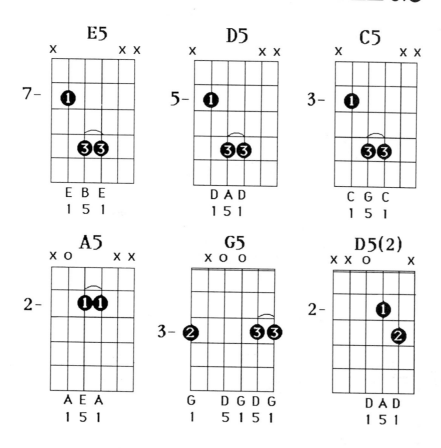

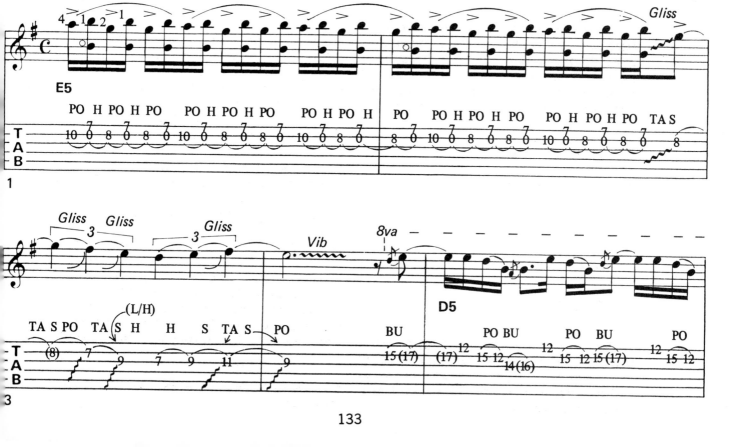

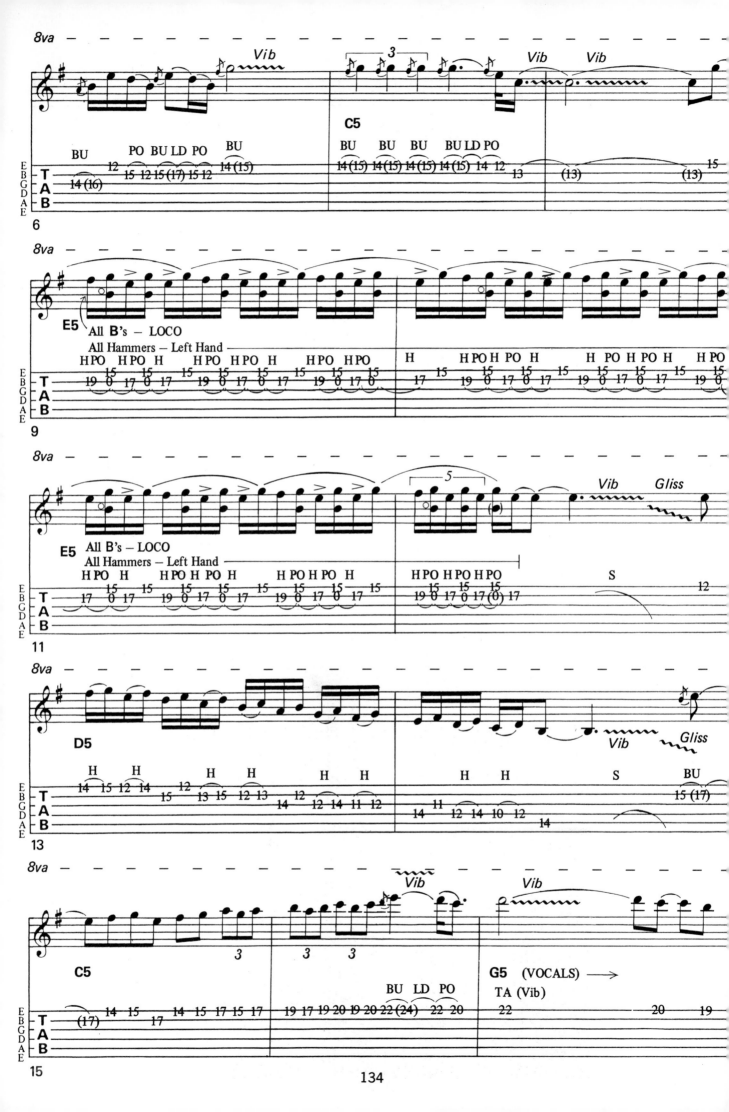

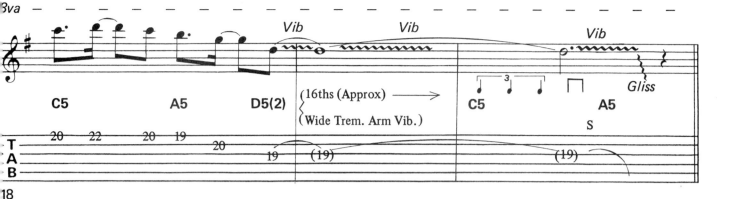

This solo uses the E aeolian mode/natural minor scale:

E  F#  G   A   B   C   D   E
1   2  b3   4   5  b6  b7   1

and the E minor pentatonic:

E   G   A   B   D   E
1  b3   4   5  b7   1

The opening phrase in bars 1-2 is a quite ingenious open string, pull off idea. To play it correctly you should hold down the B (7th fret, E string) with your right hand, first finger, then pull off with your fourth finger from the A (10th fret, B string) to the open B string. As you do this, catch the B which is held down by your first finger, so that both Bs sound at the same time. After this, simply repeat the procedure only this time hammering on and pulling off from the G to the open B. Make sure the open string doesn't sound too strongly, as the A G G accented polyrythm should take precedence.

Bars 3 and 4 contain a quarter note triplet phrase which is very reminiscent of bar 9 of Gary Moore's *Out In The Fields* solo, while bars 5-8 feature some fairly typical minor pentatonic ideas (bars 5 and 6), rounded off by a few augmented fourth (F#)-perfect fifth (G) bends.

The ideas in bars 1-2 are employed once again for the phrase which runs from bars 9-12, although this time the open Bs are sounded to an even lesser degree.

Bars 13 and 14 include a natural minor scale run which often crops up in solos and should give you good exercise in a figure that has every other note descending by an interval of a third.

In the final phrase (bars 15-20) Adrian plays an ascending run which makes good use of notes in the higher register and in so doing, brings the solo to an effective close. Notice the rhythmic figures placed under the last note (D). These indicate the phrasing of the vibrato which is produced via the tremolo arm.

From the Iron Maiden single *Wasted Years* (EMI5583). Also on the album 'Somewhere In Time'. ©1986 Iron Maiden Publishing (Overseas) Ltd/Zomba Music Publishers Ltd. For the world.

# EASY LOVER

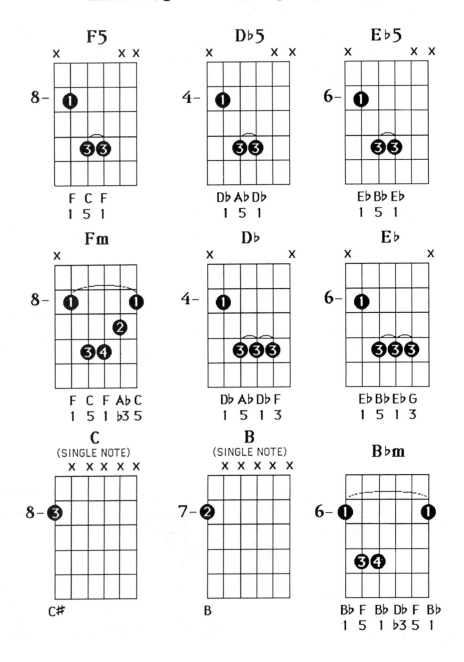

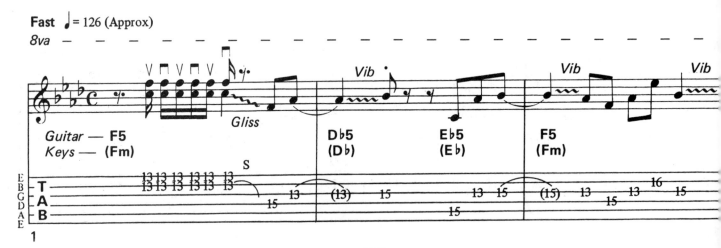

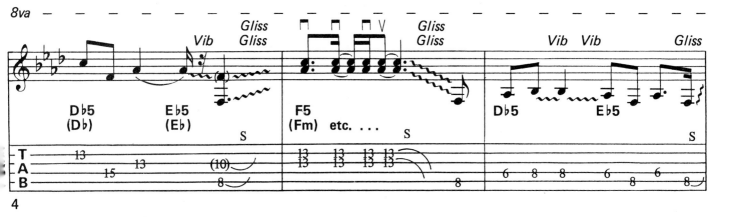

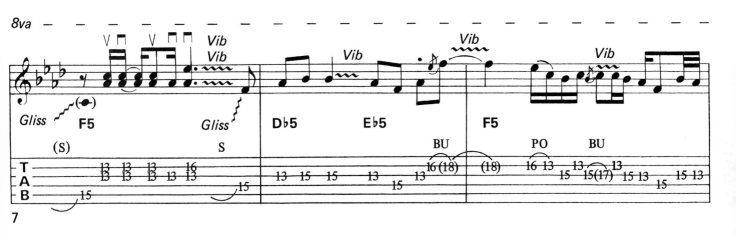

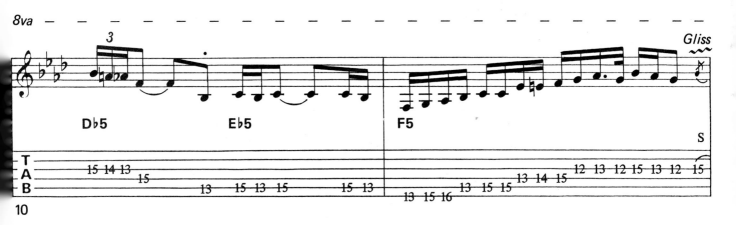

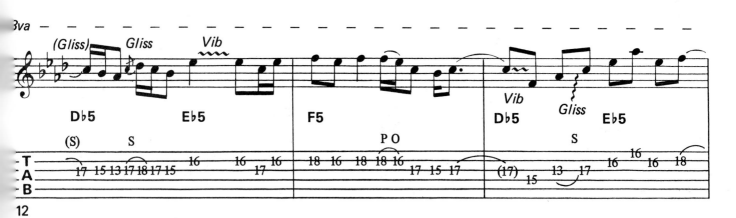

137

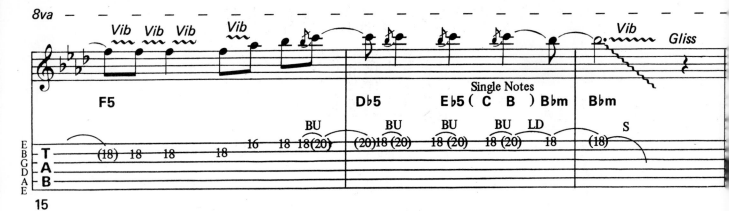

This is a fairly straightforward solo overall. The scales used include the F minor pentatonic:

F Ab Bb C Eb F
1 b3 4 5 b7 1 (bars 1-10 and 13-17)

and the F aeolian mode/natural minor scale:

F G Ab Bb C Db Eb F
1 2 b3 4 5 b6 b7 1 (bars 10-12)

although in bar 10 the A (major 3rd of F) is used in passing to decorate the pentatonic run. Similarly in bar 11, the E (major 7th of F) is used to decorate the natural minor run and this is the only section which may prove tricky. To perform it correctly you should use strict alternate picking and if you experience any problems playing it or any other part of the solo at the correct speed, I suggest you play the single at 33rpm and learn the solo in C, then move the solo up to F when you feel ready. Incidentally, to play the solo in C you should start at the 8th fret and play the notes in the same formation shown in the tab for F.

From the Phil Collins/Philip Bailey single *Easy Lover* (CBS/Virgin A4195). Also on the Philip Bailey album 'Chinese Wall' (CBS 26161). © Warner Brothers Music, Hit & Run Music.

# EDWARD VAN HALEN
# JUMP

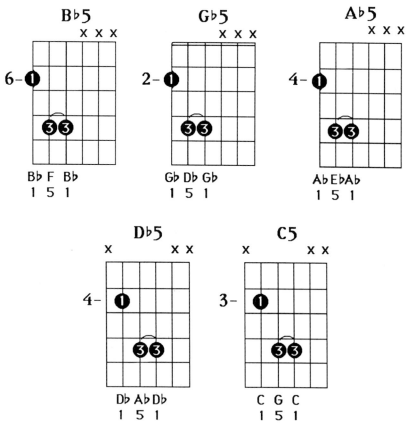

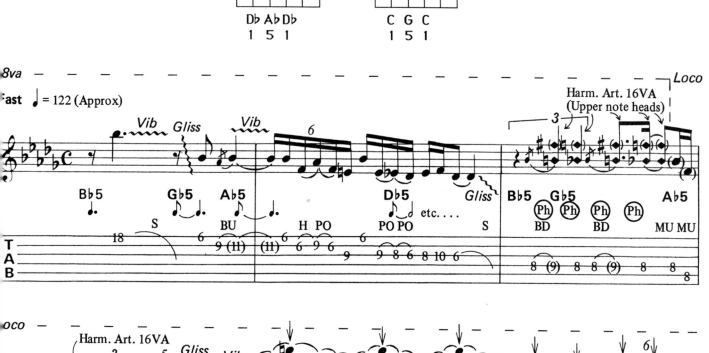

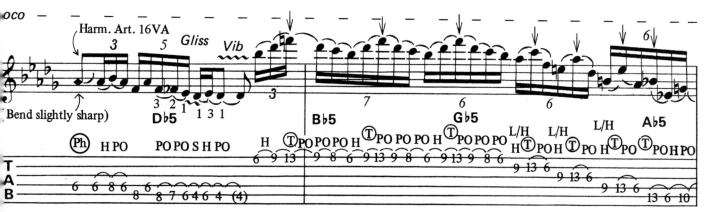

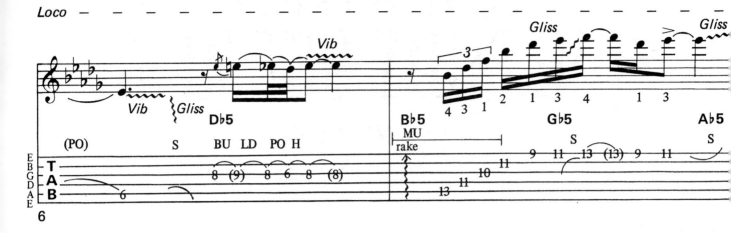

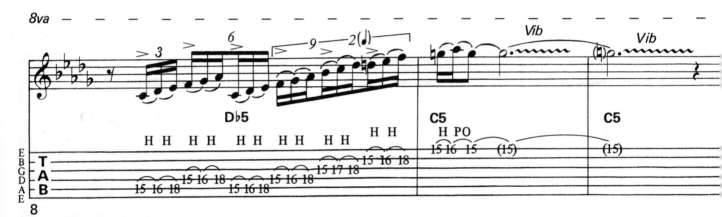

Edward Van Halen's solo from *Jump* is a fine example of his highly individualistic approach to playing, an approach which he has often very aptly described as akin to 'falling down the stairs and landing on your feet'.

Bars 1, 2, 4 and 6 all contain ideas which use notes from the Bb blues scale:

| Bb | Db | Eb | Fb | (E) | F | Ab | Bb |
|----|----|----|----|-----|---|----|----|
| 1  | b3 | 4  | b5 |     | 5 | b7 | 1  |

For the phrase in bar 3 you need to perform a series of pinched harmonics. If played correctly this should result in all the harmonics sounding two octaves and a fifth higher than the fretted notes.

Bar 5 features an example of Eddie's 'trademark' two hand tapping. This begins with a figure played on the high E string which could loosely be defined as a Bb minor add 9 arpeggio:

| Bb | Db | F | C |
|----|----|---|---|
| 1  | b3 | 5 | 9 |

This is then followed by a further series of arpeggios which descend across the B, G and D strings. These arpeggios are of three chords, F minor:

| F | Ab | C |
|---|----|---|
| 1 | b3 | 5 |

Db minor:

| Db | Fb | (E) | Ab |
|----|----|-----|----|
| 1  | b3 |     | 5  |

and Ab minor:

| Ab | Cb | (B) | Eb |
|----|----|-----|----|
| 1  | b3 |     | 5  |

Bar 7 contains another arpeggio idea using Bb minor:

| Bb | Db | F |
|----|----|---|
| 1  | b3 | 5 |

in conjunction with a right hand glide stroke and left hand slides to produce a very effective phrase. The closing phrase in bars 8-10 is a slurred run which for the most part uses notes from the C locrian mode:

| C | Db | Eb | F | Gb | Ab | Bb | C |
|---|----|----|---|----|----|----|---|
| 1 | b2 | b3 | 4 | b5 | b6 | b7 | 1 |

From the Van Halen album '1984' (9239851). ©WEA.

# EDWARD VAN HALEN
# SOMEBODY GET ME A DOCTOR

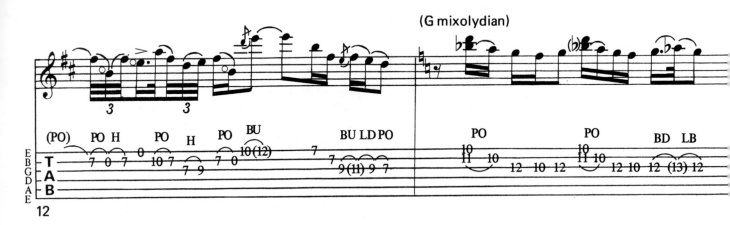

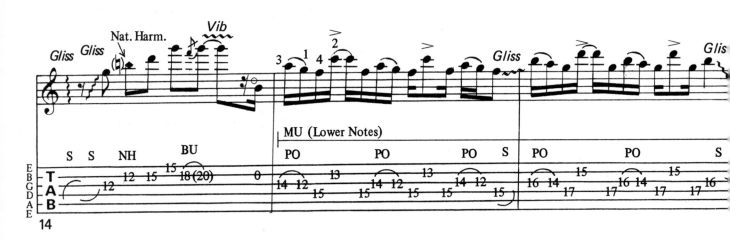

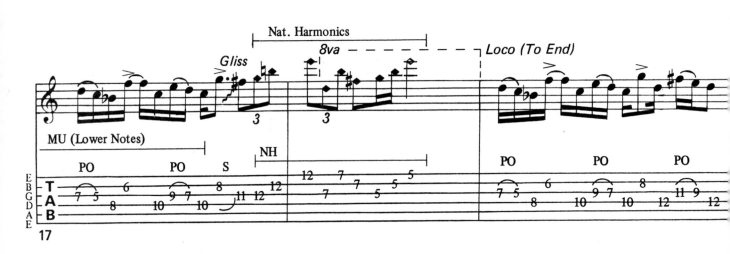

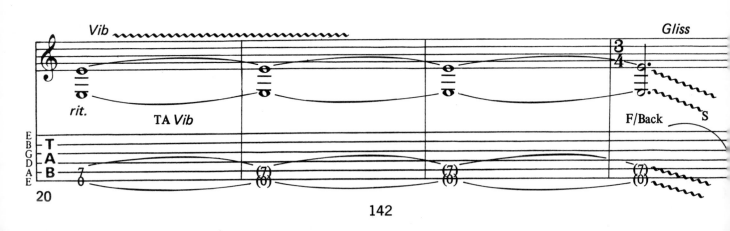

The scales used in this solo include the A dorian mode (bars 1-8):

| A | B | C  | D | E | F# | G  | A |
|---|---|----|---|---|----|----|---|
| 1 | 2 | b3 | 4 | 5 | 6  | b7 | 1 |

the B aeolian mode/natural minor scale (bars 9-12):

| B | C# | D  | E | F# | G  | A  | B |
|---|----|----|---|----|----|----|---|
| 1 | 2  | b3 | 4 | 5  | b6 | b7 | 1 |

and the G mixolydian mode:

| G | A | B | C | D | E | F  | G |
|---|---|---|---|---|---|----|---|
| 1 | 2 | 3 | 4 | 5 | 6 | b7 | 1 |

In addition to these scale forms a number of passing notes are used: Eb (b5) in bar 7, F (b5) in bars 9 and 10, Bb (b3) in bars 13, 17 and 19, and F# (major 7) in bar 19.

You may have noticed that this solo is the only one in the book which doesn't have a chordal accompaniment given. The reason for this is simply that the bass line, as played on the record, is vital to the effectiveness of this solo. You should also note that in order to avoid an unnecessary number of accidentals in the music notation, modal key signatures have been used.

During the introduction in bars 1-6 the small x's indicate a percussive effect which in this case should be produced by heavily damping the string with your right hand palm.

The phrase in bars 11-12 shows a typical Van Halen idea, whereby he uses open strings to displace the flow of melodic figures, thus producing an angular effect. As the rhythmic phrasing for this passage is extremely complex you would be well advised to consult the record prior to playing through it.

Another instantly recognisable Van Halen trait is his use of harmonics. In this solo he plays a phrase made up entirely of natural harmonics (bars 17-18). To play these correctly all the harmonics should be produced by lightly touching – not pressing down – the strings directly over the frets, as shown in the tab. You should also make sure that you lift your finger off the string immediately after each harmonic sounds.

From the Van Halen album 'Van Halen II' (K56616). ©WEA.

# STEVIE RAY VAUGHAN
# LIFE WITHOUT YOU

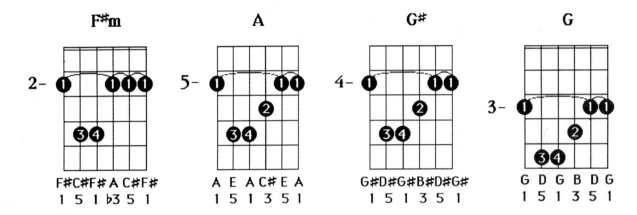

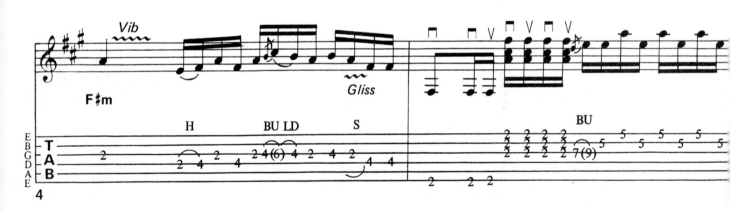

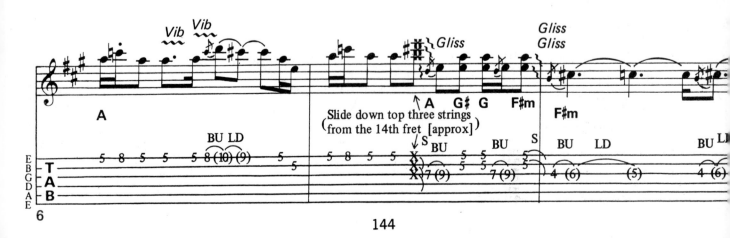

Stevie Ray Vaughan first shot to fame and received international recognition after playing on David Bowie's single *Let's Dance*. Since then he has released several albums with his band Double Trouble, all of which feature his versatile blend of blues, rock, soul and jazz guitar playing. This solo is a good example of his blues approach. It uses a combination of three different scale types, the F# blues scale:

| F# | A | B | C | C# | E | F# |
|----|----|----|----|----|----|----|
| 1 | b3 | 4 | b5 | 5 | b7 | 1 |

the A minor/major pentatonic:

| A | B | C | C# | D | E | F# | G | A |
|----|----|----|----|----|----|----|----|----|
| 1 | 2 | b3 | 3 | 4 | 5 | 6 | b7 | 1 |

and the A blues scale:

| A | C | D | Eb | E | G | A |
|----|----|----|----|----|----|----|
| 1 | b3 | 4 | b5 | 5 | b7 | 1 |

One of the most striking aspects of this solo is Stevie's total command of the blues vocabulary. Notice, for example, how freely he interchanges major and minor thirds, and flattened and perfect fifths. He also uses partial chords to 'fatten' up the sound.

Throughout the entire solo the scales used vary to correspond with the underlying chord changes, using the F# blues scale over F#m and either the Am/maj pentatonic or the A blues scale over the A chords.

The phrase in bars 17-18 should be played by picking the notes on the G string at the same time as you perform the E string bends.

Technically the solo is not unduly difficult, although to perform the piece effectively, close attention should be paid to tone control (via pickup selection and picking technique), string bending and vibrato.

# STEVE VAI
# LADIES NITE IN BUFFALO?

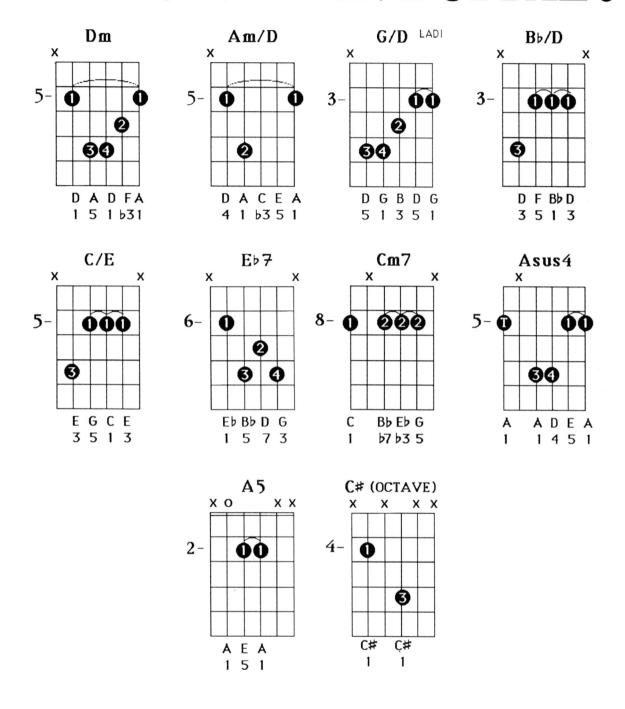

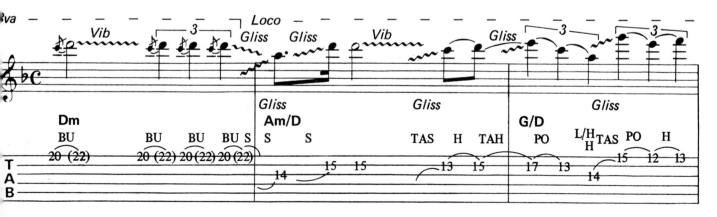

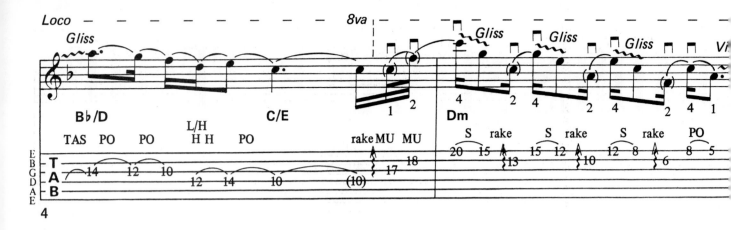

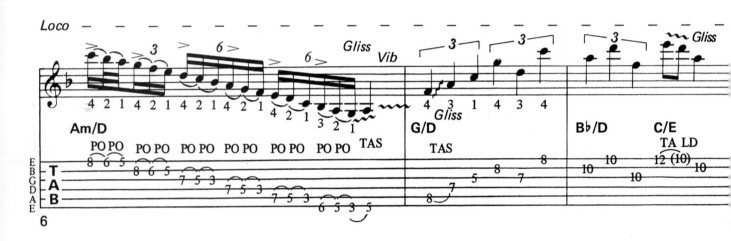

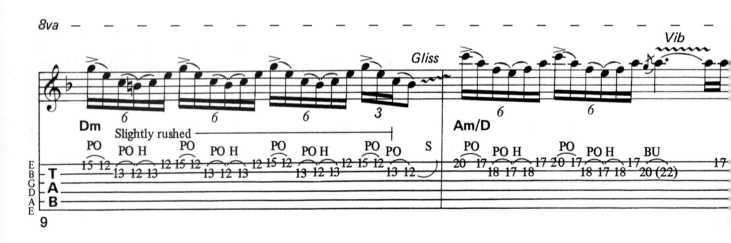

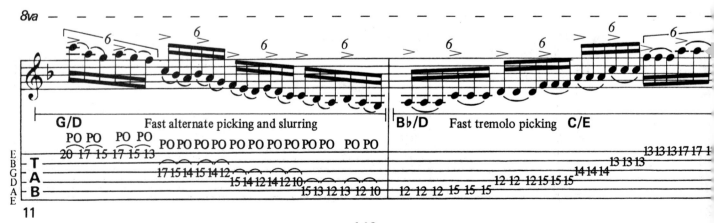

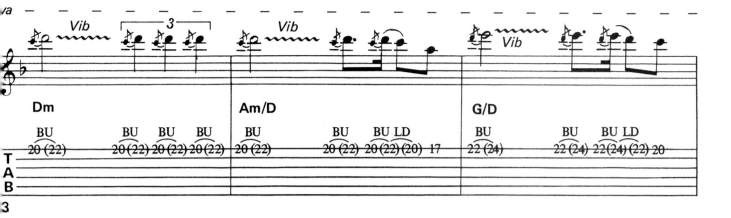

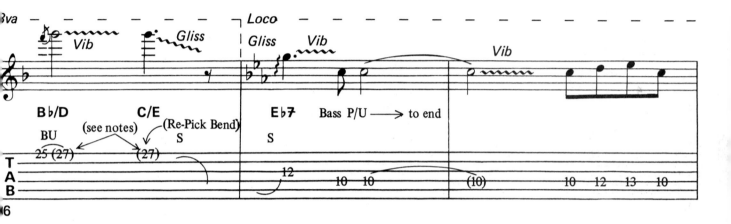

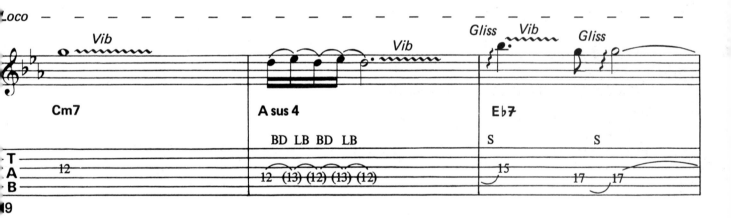

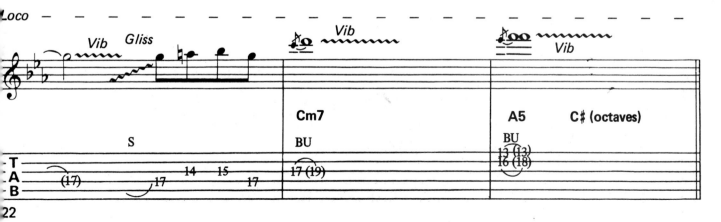

Steve Vai uses two scales for this solo, namely the D aeolian mode/natural minor scale:

| D | E | F | G | A | Bb | C | D |
|---|---|---|---|---|----|---|---|
| 1 | 2 | b3 | 4 | 5 | b6 | b7 | 1 |

for bars 1-16, and the Eb lydian mode

| Eb | F | G | A | Bb | C | D | Eb |
|----|---|---|---|----|---|---|----|
| 1 | 2 | 3 | #4 | 5 | 6 | 7 | 1 |

in bars 17-24. He only goes 'outside' these scale forms once during the entire solo, in bar 9, where the figure is played with a B (major 6th of the accompanying D chord) rather than the Bb (minor 6th) from the natural minor scale mentioned above.

The solo begins at a fairly leisurely pace, opening with some b7-key note bends (C-D) in bar 1, followed in bars 2-4 by phrases which incorporate tremolo arm glisses, combined with pull offs and normal/left hand only hammer ons.

In bar 5 things begin to get more difficult, however. This phrase uses either whole, or partial, D shape chords (F5 descending to C5, A5 and the lower F5), which are connected together via fourth finger slides. These can be fairly awkward to play with any degree of fluidity and will probably require quite a lot of practice.

The slurred run in bar 6 requires quite a large left hand stretch and a good slurring facility. The fingering I have suggested is the one I find the most comfortable, bear in mind, however, that the notes on the G, D, A and E strings could also be comfortably played using fingers 4, 3 and 1, instead of 4, 2 and 1, as indicated.

The repetitive figures in bars 9 and 10 are very reminiscent of a device often used by Gary Moore (examples of which can be found in his *Murder In The Skies* solo and his intro to *End Of The World*).

Bar 11 is, to my mind, the most demanding part of this solo. Runs of this speed are hard to execute cleanly at the best of times, but the added difficulty of having to jump to a non-adjacent string – E-G, second beat – renders this very challenging indeed. If you experience a lot of problems with this, all I can suggest is that you take your time and work initially at thoroughly memorising the fingerings and playing through the run using slurs. When you can do this at a speed approaching that of the record, start to work at incorporating the picking as well.

Bar 12 is a tremolo picked (fast alternate picking) F major (add 13) arpeggio pattern which leads into some more b7, key note bends (bar 13).

Bars 14-16 contain an ascending series of bends which end up on a bend from F-G! If you had frets that high, this would represent a bend from fret 25 up to the note found at fret 27 (as indicated in the tab), but as this is impossible on any normal guitar you have to use an alternative method, which is to either bend the string up against the bass pickup, which you can do on a Strat if the pickup height isn't too low, or fret the string on the pickup, which on a Vigier guitar was a perfect G. If these methods prove impractical due to the construction of your guitar or type of pickup, your only alternative is to fret the 13th fret of the E string (F) and bend it up a tone to G, simultaneously playing the artificial harmonic which is found in the area over, or near, the bass pickup.

The final section of the solo (bars 17-24) is a very straightforward, melodic passage in which the combined effect of the key change, the different tone produced by selecting the bass pickup and the sudden melodic and rhythmic simplicity go together to make for a very effective and memorable closing statement.

Taken from the Dave Lee Roth album 'Eat Em' And Smile' (Warner Bros UK WX56 925470-1). ©Diamond Dave Music, Warner Bros Ltd

# STEVE VAI
# SONS AND LOVERS

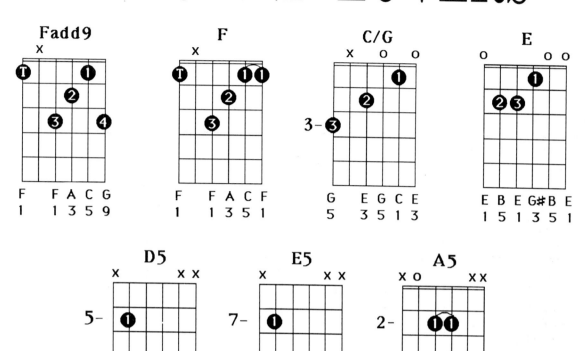

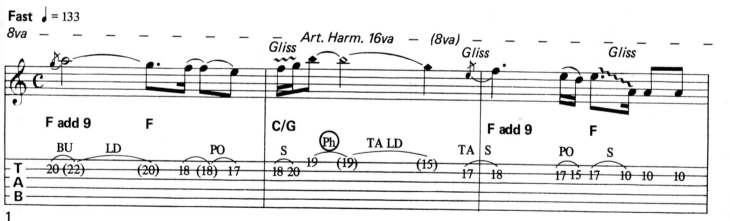

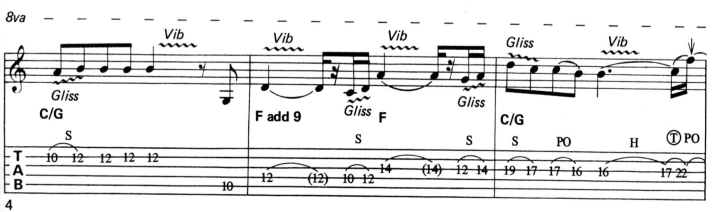

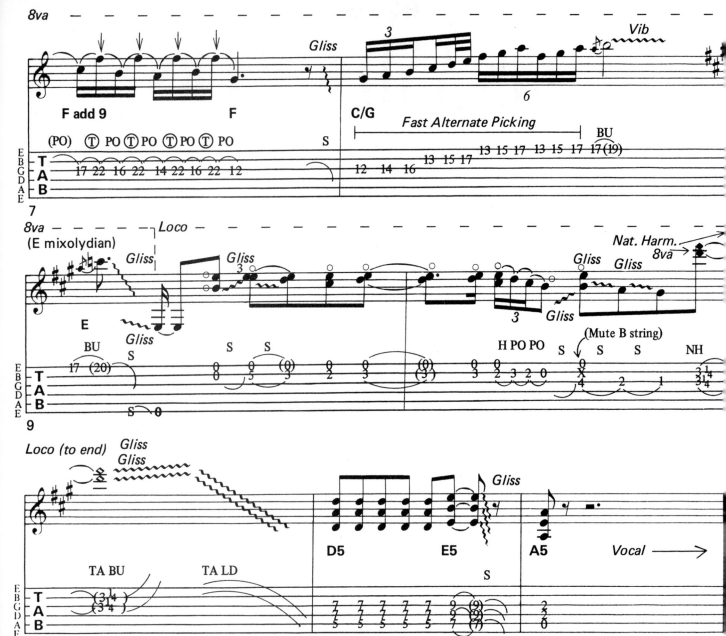

After gaining a great deal of popularity among guitarists through his work with Frank Zappa and from his own solo project 'Flexable', Steve Vai went on to join his first major heavy rock band, Alcatrazz. The solo transcribed here is taken from his first (and only) album with the band and although it isn't a very difficult solo technically speaking, it does contain many of the features which are instantly recognisable as part of Steve's unique guitar style.

Two different types of scale are used, the F lydian:

F  G  A  B  C  D  E  F
1  2  3  #4 5  6  7  1

and the E mixolydian:

E  F#  G#  A  B  C#  D  E
1  2   3   4  5  6   b7 1

Bar 2 features an extremely high pitched pinched harmonic – B, four octaves above open B. To hit this with any degree of consistency you will probably need to work out exactly where the node

point lies, and pick the string with just the right amount of attack.

The phrase in bars 4-6 is an interesting idea which combines the interval of a fifth with left hand slides to produce a very effective angular line.

Bars 6-7 feature a pedal tone of F played using two hand tapping, while the left hand simultaneously plays a descending/ascending melodic line ending on an accented ninth (G).

Bar 8 contains a very fast alternate picked run, this is probably best performed starting with a downward pick stroke.

During the final section in bars 9-13 you should allow the open strings to sustain into each other as much as possible. Also, to produce harmonics in bars 10-11 which ascend to the same degree as those on the record, you need a guitar which has had some of the wood behind the base of the tremolo routed out, thus allowing the tremolo arm to be pulled back further than normal.

From the Alcatrazz album 'Disturbing The Peace' ©

# NOTES

# NOTES

# NOTES

# NOTES

# NOTES

# NOTES

# NOTES

# NOTES